INTERPRETATION OF MASS SPECTRA

INTERPRETATION OF

MASS SPECTRA

AN INTRODUCTION

F. W. McLAFFERTY PURDUE UNIVERSITY

W. A. BENJAMIN, INC.   NEW YORK, AMSTERDAM

1967

INTERPRETATION OF MASS SPECTRA: AN INTRODUCTION

Library of Congress Catalog Card Number 66–26833
Manufactured in the United States of America

*The manuscript was put into production on March 8, 1966;
    this volume was published on November 1, 1966; second
    printing with corrections August 1967*

W. A. BENJAMIN, INC., *New York, New York 10016*

To Tibby

EDITORS' FOREWORD

Practicing organic chemists all recognize the enormous impact that modern spectroscopic methods have made on science. The change has been felt in chemistry courses as well. The teaching of chemistry always responds, if sometimes ponderously, to advances in research, but in this case a special factor is at work: Teachers of chemistry have found that both laboratory and lecture courses are much more interesting and informative by the inclusion of infrared, n.m.r., and other spectra, since these convey to the student a feeling of direct contact with experimental evidence. Even the student who will never do research using an n.m.r. spectrometer, for example, develops a much better appreciation of organic structures if n.m.r. is included in his lecture and laboratory training.

To some extent all modern organic chemistry textbooks now include material on spectroscopy. However, the treatment is necessarily incomplete, and this is true even in "comprehensive" spectroscopy books that survey a variety of techniques.

We have initiated this series on organic spectroscopy to provide single monographs for each important spectroscopic technique. The books are intended to serve both a teaching and a reference function; they contain problems, to assist the student in learning the spectroscopic method, as well as tables of data, to help him to apply the method.

The volumes in the series are intended for use by students of organic chemistry and others who wish good modern introductions into chemical spectroscopy. The volumes should be particularly useful to beginning research students. We believe that a real need exists for books at this level, and we hope that our series will be educationally stimulating.

RONALD BRESLOW
NICHOLAS J. TURRO

New York, New York
July 1966

PREFACE

The field of organic mass spectrometry has undergone an explosive growth recently; the number of publications has more than doubled in the last two years. There are now numerous references citing the solution of difficult problems in specialized research fields by the use of mass spectrometry. Instrumental developments have made it much easier for the research man without special training to obtain good spectra on a routine basis, and such instruments are now becoming available in most major research laboratories. A mass spectrum from a submicrogram sample contains a wealth of specific analytical and structural information—much more information than the expert in the field now knows how to utilize; unfortunately this abundance can discourage the novice who turns for help to compendia of mass spectral information. Yet one of the major advantages of the basic information of a mass spectrum is its simplicity. The spectrum displays masses of the ionized molecule and its fragments, and these masses are simply the sums of the masses of the component atoms.

In contrast to the books that give detailed descriptions of the mass spectra of particular types of compounds, this book has been designed especially *to teach* the interpretation of mass spectra, with emphasis on the identification of unknown compounds. The book is intended as a supplementary text for courses such as qualitative organic analysis or spectroscopic methods, and as a self-study text for scientists who are familiar with organic chemistry.

For the experienced mass spectrometrist many steps of the interpretation procedure are intuitive; this text attempts to enumerate the steps and illustrate them by application to common types of compounds. This book is not intended as a reference to spectra and fragmentation mechanisms of particular classes of compounds; such information is already available in the comprehensive volumes by Budzikiewicz, Djerassi, and Williams, and these are recommended as complementary material for this text. Similarly, other important aspects such as instruments, sample handling, and preparation of derivatives are well covered in other excellent reference volumes.

A sizable part of the book is devoted to the mechanisms of mass spectral decomposition reactions. Many mechanisms and rationalizations have been proposed previously; rather than catalog these, an attempt has been made to formulate basic rules governing these reactions, and to classify them in a few general categories. Although these generalizations may well involve some oversimplification, it is hoped that they will prove useful to the expert as well as to the novice in spectral interpretation.

This book is an outgrowth of a course that has been given six separate times to a total of over 600 scientists and students. They were required to solve unknown spectra as part of the instruction, and we feel that this is a major learning aid. The reader is urged to test his understanding of material by attempting to work the unknowns, checking his solutions with those in Chapter 10. The unknown spectra were chosen to illustrate principles of interpretation; for detailed characteristics of spectra from particular compound classes, the reader should consult the literature.

A prime objective of the book has been to show the "fun" of mass spectrometry—how the jigsaw-puzzle pieces of varying masses can be fitted together to construct an informative picture of the molecular structure. The field of interpretations and mechanisms of mass spectra is so new that it is not difficult to find fascinating areas which are virtually unexplored. In the author's opinion, the unimolecular reactions of gaseous organic ions represent an exciting new field of chemistry whose study should contribute substantially to our basic understanding of the behavior of molecules.

F. W. McLafferty

Lafayette, Indiana
July 1966

ACKNOWLEDGMENTS

The contributions of many people made this book possible. The following helped plan and teach the courses in which this material was developed: Profs. J. W. Amy, A. L. Burlingame, M. M. Bursey, D. C. DeJongh, K. L. Rinehart, S. Ställberg-Stenhagen, E. Stenhagen, and Mr. W. E. Baitinger. The following postdoctoral fellows and students read the manuscript critically and worked the problems: Drs. T. W. Shannon, Martin Senn, C. G. Warner, and R. Venkataraghavan; Miss P. C. Wszolek, Mrs. H. Hauer, and Messrs. R. D. Board, E. M. Chait, W. F. Haddon, J. G. Lawless, S. P. Levine, and L. R. Dusold. Miss Wszolek drew the bar graphs using a special recorder constructed by J. R. Barnes. I am especially indebted to Dr. Bursey for reading the manuscript critically at every stage in the production of the book, and making many valuable suggestions. Finally, I would like to express my special appreciation to Miss Sylvia Fisher for her outstanding services in typing the manuscript.

F. W. M.

CONTENTS

1

INTRODUCTION

1.1. Appearance of the Mass Spectrum

Learning how to identify a simple molecule from its mass
spectrum is much easier than from other types of spectra. The
mass spectrum shows the mass of the molecule and the masses
of the pieces from it. Thus the chemist does not have to learn
anything new—the approach is similar to an arithmetic brain-
teaser. Try one and see.

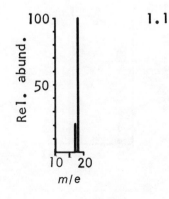

1.1

The abscissa indicates the mass (actually *m/e*, the ratio of mass to charge) and the ordinate indicates the relative abundance. If you need a hint, remember that the atomic weights of hydrogen and oxygen are 1 and 16 respectively. Check your answer (the solutions to the unknowns are given in Chapter 10).

Now try another simple spectrum; Unknown 1.2.

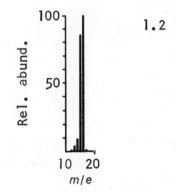

Your structure will be correct if the molecule and its pieces have masses corresponding to those of the spectrum. (Make a serious attempt to solve each unknown before looking at the solution. This is a vital part of the book's instruction.)

Unknown 1.3 contains C, H, and O atoms. Obviously the possibilities for arranging these in a molecule of molecular weight 32 are limited. Compare any molecular structure possibilities with the major peaks of the spectrum.

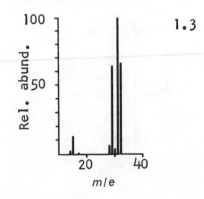

The actual recording from which the bar graph of Unknown 1.3 was made is shown in Figure 1-1. Note that for spectra from this particular spectrometer, the mass scale is ascending in the opposite direction along the abscissa, and that a small amount of Unknown 1.1 appears as an impurity. Relative abundances are determined by measuring peak heights, as these are proportional to peak areas. Unknown spectra will be displayed in this book both as bar graphs and as tabulated data. The mass spectrometer has a dynamic range of greater than 4 orders of magnitude (that is, ion abundances of 0.01% are reproducible), so that linear bar graphs must omit the low abundance data. An accurate measurement of the small peaks is important in the determination of isotopic compositions. The tabular data for Unknowns 1.1, 1.2, and 1.3 are shown here.

	Unknown 1.1		Unknown 1.2
m/e	Relative abundance	m/e	Relative abundance
1	<0.1	1	3.1
16	1.0	2	0.17
17	21.	12	1.0
18	100.	13	3.9
19	0.15	14	9.2
20	0.22	15	85.
		16	100.
		17	1.11
		18	0.01

Unknown 1.3

m/e	Relative abundance	m/e	Relative abundance
12	0.33	28	6.3
13	0.72	29	64.
14	2.4	30	3.8
15	13.	31	100.
16	0.21	32	66.
17	1.0	33	0.98
		34	0.14

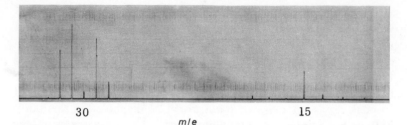

30   15

m/e

FIGURE 1-1

Some of the low intensity ions tabulated in Unknown 1.3 appear only in a more sensitive recording, as shown in Figure 1-2. The five galvanometer tracings have relative attenuations of ×1, ×3, ×10, ×30, and ×100 (bottom trace, least sensitive). The "peak" height is generally determined by measuring the number of scale divisions from the base line (top of the noise) to the top of the peak, and then multiplying this by the galvanometer attenuation.

If you inspect Figure 1-2 closely you will find other peaks which are not shown in the spectra of either Unknown 1.1 or 1.3, and are not explainable in terms of its structure. This is largely due to the "background" in the instrument — compounds which are desorbing from the walls of the instrument or are leaking in from various sources. To avoid confusion, such a "background spectrum" is usually run before the sample is actually introduced

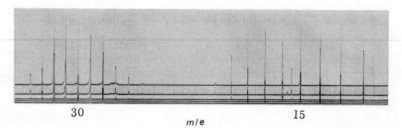

30   15

m/e

FIGURE 1-2

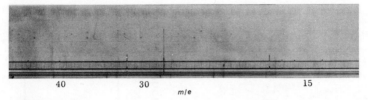

FIGURE 1-3

into the instrument.   Such a spectrum is shown in Figure 1-3.
Can you identify any of the components?   The tabulated reference spectrum of air is shown in Unknown 1.4.

Unknown 1.4

m/e	Relative abundance	m/e	Relative abundance
14	4.0	32	23.
16	0.8	33	0.02
20	0.3	34	0.09
28	100.	40	2.0
29	0.76	44	0.10

Can you assign the major peaks to the components of air?
(For now, ignore the peaks of only a few per cent relative
abundance.   Their significance will be discussed later.)
   One of the atmospheric components in its pure state gives the
spectrum of Unknown 1.5.   Can you identify it?

Unknown 1.5

m/e	Relative abundance
12	8.7
16	9.6
22	1.9
28	9.8
29	0.13
30	0.02
44	100.
45	1.2
46	0.42

1.2.   Formation of the Mass Spectrum

The discussion in this book is limited to a particular application of mass spectrometry. Complete details of the method, techniques, and instrumentation are available in a number of excellent books (1.1–1.8), reviews (1.9–1.14), and collections of data (1.15–1.18).

As in many chemical reactions used for analysis, the basic purpose of the mass spectrometer is to convert the sample into measurable products that are indicative of the original molecule. For this method the "reagent" initiating the conversion reaction is a beam of energetic (ca. 70 V) electrons. The products formed are also rather unusual — gaseous positive ions, whose masses and relative abundances are displayed in the mass spectrum.

The heart of the mass spectrometer is the *ion source,* depicted schematically in Figure 1-4. The background pressure (pressure without any sample) in the source is usually below 10^{-7} torr — roughly 10^{-10} *atm.* The bombarding electrons are "boiled off" an incandescent filament and travel through the ion chamber to an anode on the opposite side. The stream of vaporized sample molecules entering the source interacts with the beam of electrons to form a variety of products, including positive ions. These are pushed out of the source by a relatively small "repeller" (or "draw-out") potential, and then are accelerated by a large potential difference between the two electrodes shown. Small potentials can be applied to the "repeller" and "ion focus" plates to produce a defined beam of positive ions, analogously to the focusing of the light beam in a spectrophotometer. The bulk of the sample molecules and any other electron impact products are removed continuously by vacuum pumps on the ion source housing.

The collimated ion beam from the source can be separated according to the respective masses (actually, mass-to-charge ratios, m/e) of the ions by a variety of techniques, variously termed magnetic deflection, time-of-flight, radio frequency (gating), cyclotron resonance, and cycloidal focusing. Excellent

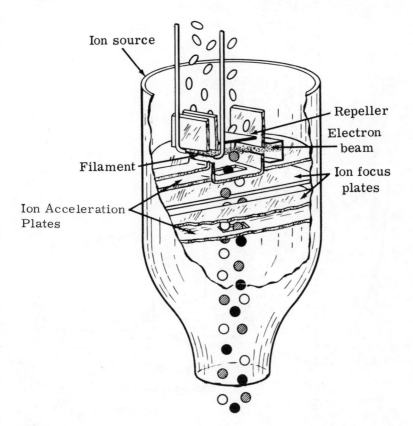

Ion source

Repeller

Electron beam

Filament

Ion focus plates

Ion Acceleration Plates

FIGURE 1-4

detailed discussions of these methods are available in the literature (*1.1*, *1.3*, *1.4*, *1.7*) or from various commercial manufacturers of these instruments. Figure 1-5 illustrates separation of the ion beam by deflection in a magnetic field, a typical single-focusing (focusing for direction) mass spectrometer.

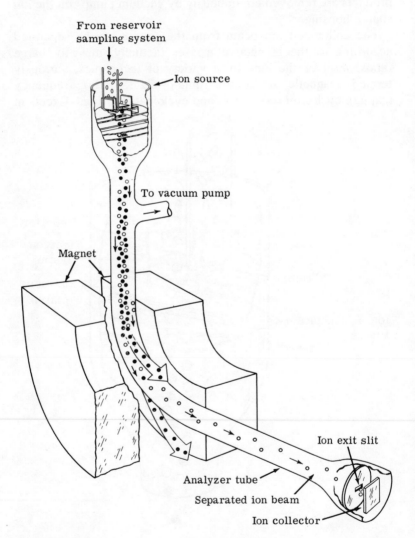

From reservoir
sampling system

Ion source

To vacuum pump

Magnet

Ion exit slit

Analyzer tube

Separated ion beam

Ion collector

FIGURE 1-5

The positive ions striking the collector produce a flow of electrons proportional to the ion abundance, and this current can be measured accurately and with great sensitivity by modern electronic techniques. Amplification of the ion signal by an electron multiplier can make possible the detection of a *single ion* arriving at the collector. Thus, although the efficiency of ionization and transmission in the mass spectrometer may only yield one ion at the collector for 10^6 sample molecules, excellent spectra can be obtained from *submicrogram* samples. Thus, the method can be used in a variety of research problems for which most of the usual structural tools do not have sufficient sensitivity.

Changing the magnetic field changes the amount of ion deflection, bringing a different m/e into focus on the collector slit. Continuously changing the magnetic field while recording the ion signals on a strip chart or similar recorder then produces a mass spectrum like Figures 1-1 to 1-3. Such scanning can also be done by varying the ion accelerating voltage — an increase in ion velocity will increase the radius of curvature of the ion path in the magnetic field, so that ions of lower m/e will be in focus at the same field setting.

The other main component of the instrument is the sample introduction system. This must produce a relatively constant flow of vaporized sample into the ion source during the spectral scan. Two general methods are used. Roughly 1 mg of sample (a large excess) can be vaporized into an evacuated, heated reservoir (Figure 1-6), from which the sample flows through a small orifice (molecular leak) into the ion source at a nearly constant rate. Because of the large pressure drop through the leak, the sample must exhibit a vapor pressure of at least 10^{-2} torr without being heated above its decomposition temperature. Recently developed fast-scanning techniques (photoplate integrative recording and oscilloscopic display, as well as high-speed recording of a fast mass sweep) greatly reduce the sample flow time necessary, and thus reduce the need of the reservoir system. This makes possible direct determination of spectra of submicrogram samples, including separated components eluted from a gas chromatograph, and also makes possible the direct vaporization of samples in the ion source. With the latter technique a mass

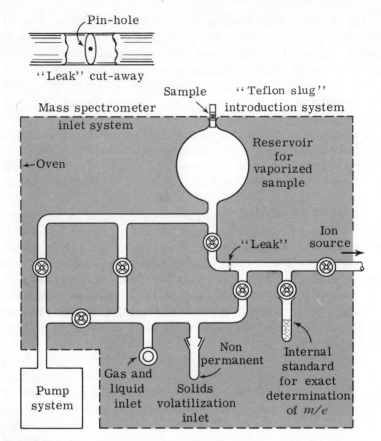

FIGURE 1-6

spectrum can now be obtained from a sample which gives a vapor pressure of only 10^{-6} torr just below its decomposition temperature, so that the method can be applied to many molecules in the 1000–2000 molecular weight range. For detailed discussions of sampling techniques a number of publications are recommended (*1.1*, *1.3*, *1.11*). Additionally, most modern analytical mass spectrometers have such systems available, and the reader is referred to the manufacturers' literature.

The main purpose of this book is to relate the positive ions formed by electron bombardment (indicated by the mass spectrum) to the molecular structure of the sample. The electron energies used are usually 50–100 V, well above the 7–16 V required for the ionization of molecules. Sample pressure in the ionization chamber is kept below 10^{-4} torr so that secondary collisions of the ions are minimized. The initial result of the electron interaction with the molecule is formation of the molecular ion by ejection of another electron. Part (sometimes essentially all) of the molecular ion decomposes further to the fragment ions of the spectrum. For example, the principal peaks in the spectrum of methanol (Unknown 1.3) are probably formed through the processes below:

$$CH_3OH + e \rightarrow CH_3OH^{+} \; (m/e \; 32) + 2e$$

$$CH_3OH^{+} \rightarrow CH_2OH^+ \; (m/e \; 31) + H\cdot$$

$$\rightarrow CH_3^+ \; (m/e \; 15) + \cdot OH$$

$$CH_2OH^+ \rightarrow CHO^+ \; (m/e \; 29) + H_2$$

The *dot* will be used to indicate a radical, so that the symbol $^{+}$ signifies a radical ion. Note that conservation of charge demands that only one ion can be formed from the decomposition of a singly charged ion. It should be reemphasized that only *unimolecular* reactions are appreciable at the operating pressure of the ion source — reactions between ions or an ion and a molecule are rarely important.

In interpreting the mass spectrum, identification of the molecular ion determines the molecular weight and often the elemental composition of the molecule. The fragment ions indicate the pieces of which the molecule is composed, and the interpreter attempts to deduce how these pieces fit together in the original molecular structure. In recent years such correlations have been achieved for the spectra of a variety of complex molecules (*1.6*).

1.3.   Standard Interpretation Procedure

You may have had difficulty with the solution of Unknown 1.5 because of apparently anomalous ions of low abundance (for example, m/e 22). Such ions can be helpful in elucidating structures, and as molecules become more complex, such help is more and more necessary. To learn to utilize the variety of information that is available in the mass spectrum, it is strongly recommended that the outline of this book be followed *step by step* in interpreting an unknown spectrum. This procedure is set forth in Table A-1 (see Appendix) in a form designed to make it useful as a checklist when one is interpreting an unknown.

This is a general, simplified approach applicable to the "average" mass spectrum. With experience the first five steps will be largely automatic and can often be done at a glance. While you are learning, however, each of the steps should be done in this order, and your postulations, assignments, and conclusions from each step should be recorded, preferably on the spectrum. If more than one explanation appears possible for a particular spectral feature, be sure to note all possibilities.

Note that Steps 1–7 of the outline correspond to Chapters 1–7. The unknowns of each chapter are designed to use *only* the steps already covered — *do not attempt* to use Table A-1 past the material which has been treated.

1.4.   Other Sample Information

It is important that all other available structural information (chemical, spectral, sample history) be incorporated into the interpretation wherever appropriate. When a sample is submitted by another research worker to the mass spectrometer laboratory for analysis, it is surprising how often other pertinent information is not transmitted. One of the strongest reasons to have the researcher interpret the mass spectra of his own samples is the importance of this information, for which the research man will have the broadest and most thorough understanding. The scientist who has interpreted infrared and nuclear magnetic resonance spectra of his own compounds should need no convincing on this point. This is also one of the main incentives for the preparation of this book — mass spectrometry should be for scientists, not just for mass spectrometrists.

1.5. Directions for Obtaining the Spectrum

Careful plans should be formulated for running the sample on the mass spectrometer. Such plans must be based on the available sample information discussed above and analytical information desired. This planning will be treated only briefly here, for much of it will be obvious after you have become familiar with the interpretation of spectra. Details are available in the general references (*1.1, 1.3, 1.12, 1.14*).

The techniques of sample handling (see Section 1.3) utilized will depend on the vapor pressure, thermal stability, and amount of the sample available, as well as the quantitative accuracy of ion abundances desired. Most nonpolar organic samples of molecular weights up to 300 or 400 can be run with the reservoir-leak system at 200°C. Direct ion source introduction is necessary for less volatile samples, for those of poor thermal stability, or for those available in submilligram quantities. (By-passing the leak and using a small reservoir are possible alternatives.) Rate of vaporization must be carefully controlled when utilizing direct ion source introduction.

Other necessary directions (when differing from the standard operating procedure) include mass range of the scan, mass ranges in which a low background is imperative, sample and ion source temperatures, and factors affecting abundance-measurement accuracy and sensitivity (scan speed, amplification). A second scan with perfluorokerosene or some other internal mass standard may be in order if mass measurement is critical or unreliable. It is sometimes desirable to run reference spectra under comparable operating conditions to differentiate between compounds of close structural similarities.

Special techniques are often necessary for transfer of the sample to the introduction system, for example, samples that are gaseous, volatile, hygroscopic, or reactive. If impurities are suspected, the sample can be fractionated into the inlet system and successive spectra compared.

Finally, proper precautions must be taken for the handling of toxic, noxious, corrosive, or otherwise dangerous samples. This is, of course, especially true if you must depend on others to run your spectra, and thus need their continuing cooperation.

Before continuing to Chapter 2, try Unknowns 1.6 to 1.9, again ignoring the small peaks adjacent to large ones.

Unknown 1.6

m/e	Relative abundance
12	0.91
13	3.6
14	0.10
24	6.1
25	23.
26	100.
27	2.15
28	0.02

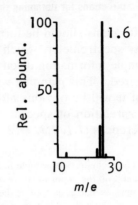

Unknown 1.7

m/e	Relative abundance
12	4.2
13	1.7
13.5	0.88
14	1.6
15	0.12
26	17.
27	100.
28	1.6
29	0.06

Unknown 1.8

m/e	Relative abundance
14	17.
15	100.
16	1.0
19	2.0
20	0.34
31	10.
32	9.3
33	89.
34	95.
35	1.1

Unknown 1.9

m/e	Relative abundance
12	3.3
13	4.3
14	4.4
15	0.07
16	1.7
28	31.
29	100.
30	89.
31	1.3
32	0.21

2

ELEMENTAL FORMULAS

The modern single-focusing analytical mass spectrometer will determine the *m/e* of a peak *to the nearest mass unit,* even for ions of masses as high as 1000. In addition, it is sometimes possible to determine the *elemental composition* of peaks. The most powerful technique for this utilizes the high resolution (double-focusing) mass spectrometer, although such measurements can be made at low masses under specialized operating conditions on modern single-focusing instruments. As an alternate not requiring this sophisticated instrumentation, the presence of isotopes of known natural abundance offers a useful and simple method for determining elemental composition for many ions.

2.1. High Resolution

Determination of the exact mass of the molecular or fragment ion can define the elemental composition directly. The monoisotopic atomic weights of the nuclides are not exact whole numbers on the basis of carbon $(C^{12}) = 12.000000$ (Table 2-1), so

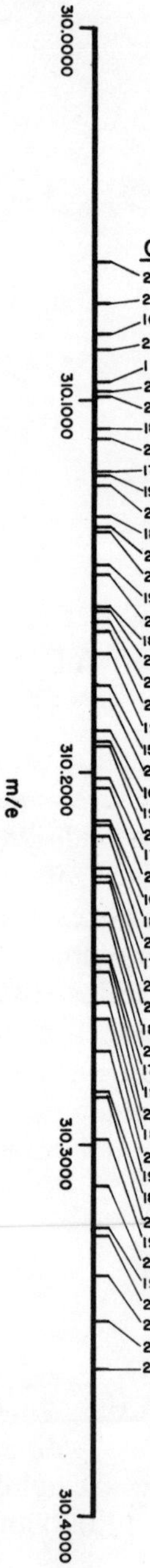

	C	H	N	O	Δ m.m.u.
	21	10	0	3	296.9
	20	10	2	2	285.7
	16	12	3	4	277.2
	21	12	1	2	273.1
	17	14	2	4	264.6
	20	12	3	1	262.0
	22	14	0	2	260.6
	18	16	1	4	252.0
	21	14	2	1	249.3
	17	16	3	3	240.8
	19	18	0	4	239.4
	22	16	1	1	236.7
	18	18	2	3	228.2
	21	16	3	0	225.6
	23	18	0	1	224.2
	19	20	1	3	215.6
	22	18	2	0	212.9
	18	20	3	2	204.4
	20	22	0	3	203.0
	23	20	1	0	200.4
	24	22	0	0	197.8
	19	22	2	2	191.8
	15	24	3	4	183.3
	20	24	1	2	179.2
	16	26	2	4	170.7
	19	24	3	1	168.1
	21	26	0	2	166.7
	17	28	1	4	158.1
	20	26	2	1	155.4
	16	28	3	3	146.9
	18	30	0	4	145.5
	21	28	1	1	142.8
	17	30	2	3	134.3
	20	28	3	0	131.7
	22	30	0	1	130.3
	18	32	1	3	121.7
	21	30	2	0	119.0
	17	32	3	2	110.5
	19	34	0	3	109.1
	22	32	1	0	106.5
	18	34	2	2	97.9
	23	34	0	0	93.9
	19	36	1	2	85.3
	18	36	3	1	74.1
	20	38	0	2	72.8
	19	38	2	1	61.5
	20	40	1	1	48.9
	19	40	3	0	37.7
	21	42	0	1	36.4
	20	42	2	0	25.1
	21	44	1	0	12.6
	22	46	0	0	0

(MASS 310.3599)

FIGURE 2-1

16

that sufficiently careful mass measurements can distinguish between isobaric ions. "Isobaric" is used here to define ions that are of the same weight *to the nearest whole mass number.*

TABLE 2-1.   *Exact Nuclidic Masses*

Isotope	Atomic weight	Isotope	Atomic weight
H^1	1.007825	F^{19}	18.998405
H^2	2.014102	Si^{28}	27.976929
C^{12}	12.000000	P^{31}	30.973765
C^{13}	13.003354	S^{32}	31.972073
N^{14}	14.003074	Cl^{35}	34.968851
O^{16}	15.994915	Br^{79}	78.918329
O^{18}	17.999160	I^{127}	126.904470

Figure 2-1 shows the exact mass of a variety of possible ions of molecular weight 310 containing carbon, hydrogen, not more than three nitrogen atoms, and not more than four oxygen atoms (*1.2, 2.1*).

> Because most laboratories with double-focusing high resolution instrumentation are already well versed in spectral interpretation, the techniques involved will not be discussed here (*2.2, 2.3*). Automatic techniques of exact mass measurement and formula computation can list the ions directly according to their elemental composition (*2.1, 2.4*). With modern single-focusing analytical mass spectrometers, such elemental composition determinations are possible for low molecular weight ions, using careful (and tedious) measurements (*2.5*).

Most of the discussion and examples of this book will assume that high resolution capability is not available on a routine basis, although most of the basic principles of spectral interpretation are the same.

2.2.   Verification of Mass Assignments

It is very important that the masses assigned on the spectrum are *correct* — an error of one mass unit can seriously confuse the interpretation. (Such verification will not be necessary to solve the unknowns in this book, but it is of great practical importance

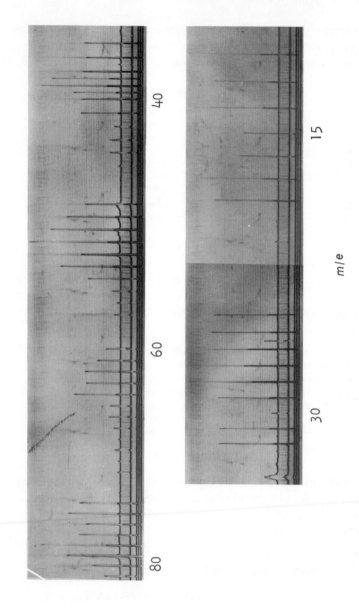

m/e

FIGURE 2-2

in solving an actual unknown spectrum.) With most mass spectrometers you should be able to determine the *exact unit mass* of each ion for masses well above the "resolving power" quoted by the manufacturer for the instrument. Many modern analytical mass spectrometers have resolving powers above 1000, so for all peaks ordinarily encountered the unit mass should be exactly determinable. (Monoisotopic atomic weights are sufficiently close to whole numbers so that with single-focusing instruments almost all ions will appear nominally at whole number masses. Thus molecular and fragment ion weights are generally counted and recorded as whole numbers.)

If there is a mass indicator on your mass spectrometer, become familiar with its reliability by running the spectra of known compounds. With peaks for which an accurate mass measurement is critical, rerun the spectrum of the unknown compound simultaneously with a known compound whose spectrum gives a peak nearly adjacent in mass. Perfluorokerosene is convenient for this as it gives characteristic peaks throughout the spectrum and is quite volatile (*2.6*).

If the instrument has no mass marker, a standard mass scanning speed and chart paper speed should be used to obtain spectra so that the abscissa scale will remain nearly constant from spectrum to spectrum. It is convenient to construct a paper mass ruler from the known peaks of a perfluorokerosene or other reference spectrum. A simple trimming adjustment on either the mass scanning speed control or the chart paper drive can help compensate for day-to-day variations.

To verify the m/e of the ions, start at the low mass end of the spectrum. The approximate m/e can be estimated from the instrument settings, and should be marked on the spectrum when it is run. A further check can usually be made on background peaks, since it is very difficult to get all traces of air and moisture out of an instrument (see Figure 1-3). For quadrupole and cyclotron resonance (omegatron) spectrometers, the scale is linear with m/e. For magnetic and time-of-flight instruments, the m/e scale is usually proportional to $(m/e)^{1/2}$, that is, masses 16, 25, 36, 49, 64, and so on are regularly spaced. Keeping in mind the relationship of mass to distance along the abscissa, count up in mass for the peaks shown in the spectrum of pyridine, Figure 2-2. What is the m/e of the most abundant ion in the spectrum?

For spectra with more sparsely spaced ions, a mass ruler as described above is handy to carry the count across blank regions of the spectrum, but the mass ruler should be referenced to the actual peaks in the spectrum as often as possible during the counting. Temperature, hysteresis, and other magnet instabilities can cause hourly variations in the accuracy of such a mass ruler. The dynamic recording range of the mass spectrometer is so great, however, that there are usually sufficient peaks to make such a counting technique quite accurate. Watch for two types of peaks that often appear at nonintegral masses, and therefore may lead to an erroneous count. Multiply charged ions can appear at fractional masses; for example, a doubly charged ion of mass 79 will appear at m/e 79/2, or 39.5. So-called "metastable ions" can also appear as fractional masses, but these can be easily recognized by their characteristic width and diffuseness as compared to a regular peak. Note m/e 34.2 in Figure 2-2. Such peaks are very helpful to indicate particular reaction paths; their use is discussed later.

2.3.   Natural Isotopic Abundances; Isotopic Clusters

A chemically pure compound usually gives a mixture of mass spectra because the elements that compose it are not isotopically pure. Table A-2 (see Appendix) shows that some elements have more than one isotope of appreciable natural abundance. A second isotope makes an especially prominent appearance in the spectrum if it is more than one unit higher in mass than the more abundant isotopic species. Bromine and chlorine, and to a lesser extent silicon and sulfur, are striking common examples. The presence of these elements in an ion is often easily rec-

Unknown 2.1

m/e	Relative abundance
35	12.
36	100.
37	4.1
38	33.
39	0.01

ognized from the "isotopic clusters" produced in the spectrum. Thus the elemental composition of Unknown 2.1 can be recognized from the characteristic 3/1 isotopic ratio of the ions separated by two mass units. (Again, ignore ions of low relative abundance. Their significance will be explained later in this chapter.)

Determination of the elemental composition can provide the key to the solution of Unknown 2.2 also. Again ignore the small peaks next to the large ones.

Unknown 2.2

m/e	Relative abundance	m/e	Relative abundance
12	1.2	48	0.95
13	1.4	79	10.
14	3.8	81	10.
15	59.	91	4.2
39.5	0.19	92	2.4
40.5	0.20	93	6.8
46	1.3	94	100.
46.5	0.30	95	3.5
47	2.3	96	96.
47.5	0.28	97	1.1

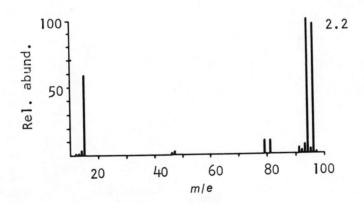

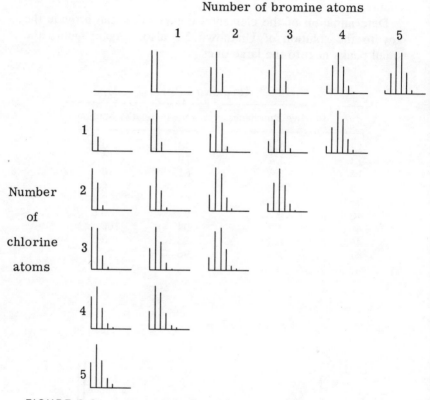

FIGURE 2-3 *"Isotopic clusters" resulting from combinations of up to five chlorine and five bromine atoms.*

If there is more than one atom of these elements present in the molecule, the result is even more striking. For hydrogen bromide the isotopic molecular ions at m/e 80 and 82 (HBr^{79} and HBr^{81}) are in the relative proportions of roughly 1/1. The mass spectrum of Br$_2$ shows prominent (molecular) ions at masses 158, 160, and 162 of relative abundances 1/2/1 due to the ions Br$_2$^{79}, Br^{79}Br^{81}, and Br$_2$^{81}, respectively. In a similar fashion, any ion structure containing three bromine atoms will exhibit four peaks at intervals of two mass units in the ratio 1/3/3/1. The characteristic patterns resulting from combinations of the chlorine and bromine isotopes are illustrated by the bar graphs of Figure 2-3. Details of the calculations of these ratios are given in the comprehensive text by Beynon (_1.1_).

> A common source of confusion is that the mass ascribed to "the molecular ion" of a compound is _not_ usually that of the peak at highest mass, and sometimes is not even the most abundant of the various isotopic forms of the molecular ion. By convention, mass spectrometrists calculate the molecular weight of a compound on the basis of the mass of the most abundant isotope of each of the elements present. For benzene (C_6H_6), which has a substantial m/e 79 and a m/e 80 peak, the molecular ion is considered to be at mass 78 (C = 12, H = 1). For compounds containing a number of chlorine and (or) bromine atoms, the situation can be even more confusing. The molecular weight of the molecule Br$_2$ is considered to be 158, twice the mass of the most abundant isotope, Br^{79}. However, in the mass spectrum of Br$_2$, the most abundant ion is at m/e 160, as the relative abundance of the Br^{79}Br^{81} is almost twice that of the Br$_2$^{79}.

2.4. Carbon and Oxygen Atom Content

The mass spectrum of chemically pure carbon dioxide, Unknown 1.5, is a composite of the spectra of $C^{12}O_2{}^{16}$, $C^{13}O_2{}^{16}$, $C^{12}O^{16}O^{18}$, and so on. The molecular ions for these three molecules are at m/e 44, 45, and 46, respectively. Although the presence of this mixture makes the spectrum more complicated, again the abundances of the isotopic components give a direct indication of the elemental composition. From the natural abundances of carbon isotopes (Table A-2) it would be expected that carbon dioxide would show $C^{12}O_2^{16}/C^{13}O_2^{16}$ of $100/1.08$. The relative abundance of the m/e 45 peak in Unknown 1.5 reflects in addition a small contribution from $C^{12}O^{16}O^{17}$. Because a molecular ion of m/e 46 will be formed if either of the oxygen atoms of CO_2 is an O^{18}, the relative abundance of $C^{12}O^{16}O^{18}$ molecules is *twice* that of the O^{18} atoms.

In Unknown 2.3 calculate the maximum number of carbon atoms in the ion of m/e 43. What isotopic abundance shows that this ion cannot have the elemental composition $C_2H_3O^+$? (To

Unknown 2.3

m/e	Relative abundance	m/e	Relative abundance
1	1.11	37	1.01
2	0.10	37.1 m	0.06
12	0.13	38	1.89
13	0.26	39	12.5
14	0.96	39.2 m	0.46
15	5.30	40	1.63
16	0.12	41	27.8
19 d	0.04	42	12.2
19.5 d	0.01	43	100.
20 d	0.02	44	3.33
24	0.03	45	0.05
24.1 m	0.01	48	0.06
25	0.46	49	0.40
25.1 m	0.11	50	1.29
25.5 d	0.36	51	1.05
26	6.17	52	0.26
26.5 d	0.08	53	0.74
27	37.1	54	0.19
27.5 d	0.05	55	0.93
28	32.6	56	0.72
29	44.2	57	2.42
30	0.98	58	12.3
30.4 m	0.14	59	0.54
31.9 m	0.20	60	0.01
35.1 m	0.02		
36	0.08		

(m) "metastable" peak (see Section 6.1)
(d) doubly charged ions.

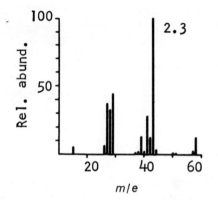

illustrate the multiplicity of peaks actually found in a spectrum, the complete spectrum (*1.17*) has been included in this case. The significance of the "metastable" and doubly charged ions will be discussed later.) Note that the C^{13} probability for *each* carbon atom in an ion is 1.08%; thus for an ion containing 10 carbon atoms the probability of *any one* carbon atom being a C^{13} is $10 \times 1.08\% = 10.8\%$.

Convenient formulas for these calculations are shown in Table A-2 with examples of their application. The factor of 1.1% per carbon atom is used for convenience and to correct for the small contribution of deuterium from the usual hydrogen content of the ion (*1.3*). Notice that this equation gives the *maximum* number of atoms of each type in the elemental composition. Presence of interfering ions from any source, such as other fragment ions, impurities, or background, will cause the indicated number of ions to be erroneously high. In Unknown 2.3, calculating the number of carbon atoms of *m/e* 41 from the relative abundance of ions in *m/e* 42 gives a ridiculously high number of carbon atoms. This technique, then, can only be applied to "clean" portions of the spectrum. Try assigning elemental compositions to other major ions in Unknown 2.3 where this technique can be applied.

Note that in Unknown 2.3 the singly charged "nonmetastable" ions appear in series starting at *m/e* 12, 24, 36, and 48, even though these particular ions are of very low abundance. These are actually the unsubstituted telomeric carbon ions C^+, C_2^+, C_3^+, and C_4^+, respectively. Such ion series are often *misleading*—it is best not to use them for determining elemental composition. Higher series tend to overlap (C_7^+ and $C_6H_{12}^+$ are both *m/e* 84), as do heteroatom-containing ions. Introduction of functional groups usually lowers the abundance of the initial unsubstituted ions of each series to unobservable levels, and, most seriously, such ions are often rearranged.

2.5.   Rings plus Double Bonds

Because of the valencies of the elements involved, the total number of rings and double bonds in a molecule of the formula $C_xH_yN_zO_n$ will be equal to $x - 1/2y + 1/2z + 1$. For ions, the calculated value may end in "1/2" and this fraction should be subtracted to obtain the true value (*2.7*). Use of this should be more obvious by inspection of the examples in Table A-2. The value 4 found for pyridine represents the ring and three double bonds of this molecule, while the 5.5 calculated for the benzoyl ion represents the ring, the three double bonds of benzene, and the double bond of the carbonyl group. Calculate the number of rings and double bonds for the empirical formulas that you found for *m/e* 43 and 58 in Unknown 2.3.

> If other elements are present, these are counted as additional atoms of the element C,H,N, or O to which they correspond in valency. Thus, the number of silicon atoms should be added to the number of carbon atoms, the number of halogen atoms to the number of hydrogen atoms, and the number of phosphorus atoms to the number of nitrogen atoms. Note also that this is based on the lowest valence state of the elements, and does not count double bonds formed to elements in higher valence states. Thus, the formula indicates one double bond in CH_3NO_2 (nitromethane), and no double bonds in $CH_3SO_2CH_3$ (dimethyl sulfone).

Calculate the elemental composition of the principal ions in Unknowns 2.4 through 2.9. How much can be concluded concerning the structures of these molecules from this information? Attempt to solve these unknowns. All of the spectra exhibit molecular ions.

Unknown 2.4

m/e	Relative abundance
16	5.2
24	0.8
24.5	0.01
25	0.04
32	11.
33	0.10
34	0.42
48	49.
49	0.41
50	2.3
64	100.
65	0.88
66	4.9
67	0.04

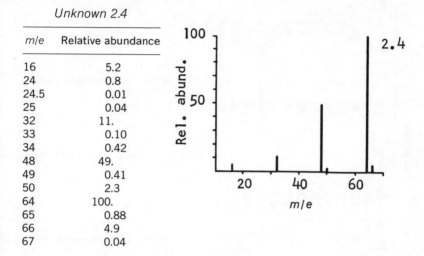

Unknown 2.5

m/e	Relative abundance
14	5.2
15	0.02
19	8.4
33	42.
34	0.15
52	100.
53	0.39
71	30.
72	0.11

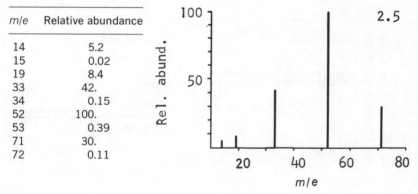

Unknown 2.6

m/e	Relative abundance	m/e	Relative abundance
24	1.3	37	0.8
25	5.7	38	0.34
26	22.	47	2.5
27	77.	48	1.2
28	1.5	49	0.92
29	0.02	50	0.37
30	0.12	59	1.5
30.5	0.24	60	5.8
31	0.16	61	8.7
31.5	0.09	62	100.
32	0.06	63	4.8
35	2.2	64	31.
36	1.0	65	0.71

2.6

Unknown 2.7

m/e	Relative abundance	m/e	Relative abundance
26	1.2	40	28.
27	2.5	41	1.2
28	1.5	50	1.8
31	4.9	51	2.5
31.5	1.3	61	4.3
32	2.2	62	6.8
32.5	0.9	63	10.
33	2.1	64	1.9
33.5	0.11	65	49.
37	4.4	66	100.
38	8.2	67	5.6
39	32.	68	0.18

2.7

Unknown 2.8

m/e	Relative abundance	m/e	Relative abundance
25	5.2	45	32.
26	38.	46	2.5
26.5	0.15	47	0.18
27	74.	52	1.4
27.5	0.26	53	6.0
28	12.	54	2.3
29	4.3	55	74.
30	0.13	56	2.6
31	0.48	57	0.29
41	1.2	71	4.3
42	1.3	72	100.
43	5.8	73	3.5
44	14.	74	0.48

2.8

Unknown 2.9

m/e	Relative abundance	m/e	Relative abundance
15	3.7	43	2.7
27	3.3	44	0.29
28	4.1	55	2.0
29	3.6	56	2.7
30	6.2	57	5.6
31	0.10	58	100.
39	4.8	59	3.6
40	1.4	60	0.05
41	18.	73	0.41
42	11.	74	0.02

2.9

3

RADICAL IONS

Ionization of the sample molecule occurs through the loss of an electron, and therefore the molecular ion is a radical species. Such an ion, either molecular or fragment, with an unpaired electron is called an "odd-electron" ion (2.6, 3.1), and designated by the symbol $\dagger$ (1.6, 3.2). It is often useful and convenient in explaining and classifying ion decomposition reactions to distinguish between such radical ions and "even-electron" ions, those in which the outer shell electrons are fully paired (1.11, 3.3). The formation and the decomposition of odd-electron ions are in general more meaningful for structure determination than the corresponding reactions of even-electron ions. It is useful to classify reactions according to the types of ions that are involved. For this symbolism, recently suggested by Shannon (3.2), it is important to remember that $^+$ refers *only* to even-electron ions.

Hanuš and Dolejš have pointed out (3.4) that the symbolism † may mislead the reader by indicating an extra electron in addition to those which the formula represents. For saturated molecules such an interpretation will be obviously erroneous, since it describes a negative ion, such as $CH_4 + e \rightarrow CH_4^{\overline{\cdot}}$, but caution is necessary for unsaturated systems. Table 3-1, which gives

TABLE 3.1. Examples of Odd-Electron and Even-Electron Ions

	Odd-electron		Even-electron	
	Delocalized charge	Localized charge	Delocalized charge	Localized charge
Aliphatic	$(CH_3CH_2CH_3)^{+\cdot}$	$CH_3CH_2\overset{+}{C}H_3$		$CH_3CH_2\overset{+}{C}H_2$
Unsaturated	$(CH_3CH{=}CH_2)^{+\cdot}$	$CH_3\overset{+}{C}H{-}\overset{\cdot}{C}H_2$	$H_2C{\cdots}\overset{+}{C}{\cdots}CH_2$ over $\overset{\mid}{H}$	$CH_2{=}CH{-}\overset{+}{C}H_2 \leftrightarrow \overset{+}{C}H_2{-}CH{=}CH_2$
Phenyl				
Aromatic			$(C_7H_7^+, \text{tropylium})$	
Heteroatoms	$(RCH_2NH_2)^{+\cdot}$	$RCH_2\overset{+\cdot}{N}H_2$		$CH_2{=}\overset{+}{N}H_2 \leftrightarrow \overset{+}{C}H_2{-}NH_2$
	$(R_2C{=}O)^{+\cdot}$	$R_2\overset{+\cdot}{C}{=}O$		$R{-}\overset{+}{C}{=}O \leftrightarrow R{-}\overset{+}{C}{=}O$

examples of the two types of ions, should clarify any such misconception. Several possible representations are given for some of the ions. Experimental information concerning the true ion structure is fragmentary and controversial; for example, the $C_6H_5^+$ ion may be acyclic or a diradical.

3.1. Abundant Odd-Electron Ions

Because of their importance in interpreting the spectrum, the major odd-electron ions should be clearly identified. Until you can recognize these "on sight" with facility, mark on the spectrum all the radical ions that are abundant compared to ions of neighboring masses. *An odd-electron ion will be at an even-numbered m/e unless it contains an odd number of nitrogen atoms.* As examples, check the spectra that have been given. Of course, determination of the elemental composition tells whether an ion is an odd- or even-electron species, for example, CH_3OH^{+} *(m/e* 32), CH_2OH^+, CH_2O^{+}, CHO^+, CH_3^+, CH_2^{+}, and $CH_3NH_2^{+}$ *(m/e* 31), $CH_2NH_2^+$ *(m/e* 30). The absence of nitrogen atoms may also be known through structural information from other sources. Abundant odd-electron ions are much less probable than even-electron ions, especially at the low mass end of the spectrum. Odd-electron ions generally are not found in a homologous series of the type separated by 14 (or 2) mass units. Such series are typical of even-electron ions.

Unknown 3.1. Indicate whether ions of the following formulas are odd-electron or even-electron: C_2H_4, C_3H_7O, C_4H_9N, C_4H_8-NO, C_7H_5ClBr, C_6H_4OS, $C_{29}F_{59}$, H_3O, and C_3H_9SiO. Which of these ions will appear at even mass numbers?

3.2. The Molecular Ion

Probably the most valuable information used in interpreting the mass spectrum is the mass and elemental composition of the molecular ion, M^{+} (also commonly called the "parent peak," although we prefer to use the latter to signify any precursor ion). In the mass spectrum of a pure compound, the molecular ion, if present, must be found at the highest *m/e* in the spectrum. Unfortunately, for a number of types of compounds, the molecular ion is not sufficiently stable to be found in appreciable abundance in the spectrum. Thus, it is possible that the peak at highest *m/e* is not $M^{\ddagger}$. There are tests that can be applied to the peak at highest mass which can demonstrate that it is not the molecular ion, although these tests cannot demonstrate the converse.

As explained in Section 2.3, mass spectrometrists calculate the molecular weight of a compound on the basis of the most abundant isotopes. However, the mixture of molecular ions possible usually makes the peak of highest mass actually due to a $M^{\ddagger}$ from less abundant isotopes. Proper elucidation of the elemental composition of $M^{\ddagger}$ will avoid confusion because of this.

MISLEADING HIGHEST MASS PEAKS. A common possibility is that the peak of highest mass may be an artifact caused by an impurity, spectrometer background, or an ion-molecule reaction. If the first is suspected, further purification can be carried out. It is often convenient to fractionate the sample in the mass spectrometer by partial vaporization; allowing only part of the sample to vaporize into the instrument will increase the contribution of the more volatile components to the spectrum. Background scans should always be run before each sample. Background peaks from adsorbed materials may increase substantially when a new sample is introduced because the new sample displaces the background material from the inlet system walls. If the sample pressure in the ion source becomes too high, secondary reactions of the ions with molecules can become appreciable. Such ion-molecule reactions give rise to peaks above the molecular weight, and some types of molecules have a high cross section for such reactions (see Section 3.3). Such ions can be identified by their relative increase with increased sample pressure or with lower ion draw-out (repeller) potentials.

ODD-ELECTRON ION REQUIREMENT. If the ion at the highest *m/e* is an even-electron ion, it cannot be the molecular ion, and thus there is no molecular ion peak in the spectrum. If the ion of highest *m/e* is at an odd mass number, to be the molecular ion it must contain an odd number of nitrogen atoms.

LOGICAL MASS DIFFERENCES TO NEIGHBORING MAJOR IONS.
There are only a limited number of neutral fragments of low mass
which are commonly lost in decompositions of molecular ions.
The presence of another major ion separated from the highest
mass ion by an anomalous mass or elemental formula will indicate that the latter ion is not the molecular ion. Presence of an
abundant (as compared to its neighboring ions) ion 5 mass units
below the ion of highest m/e would have to represent the loss of
five hydrogen atoms—a highly unlikely decomposition. A
common small neutral fragment lost from the molecular ion is
the methyl radical. For example, $C_5H_{12}^+$ (m/e 72) can yield
$C_4H_9^+$ (m/e 57) by loss of $CH_3\cdot$. However, an abundant
$(M - CH_2)^+$ is very rare. (CF_2: has a sufficiently higher stability than CH_2: so that $(M - CF_2)^+$ ions are significant for
perfluoro aromatics.) Thus, the presence of a major ion of
m/e 58 would indicate that an m/e 72 ion could not be the
molecular ion even if it were at the highest mass in the spectrum.
Such a mass difference of CH_2 is commonly encountered when
two such homologous ions are produced by decomposition of a
larger ion; for example, $C_2H_5C(CH_3)_2NH_2^+$ (m/e 87) gives both
$C_4H_{10}N^+$ (m/e 72) and $C_3H_8N^+$ (m/e 58).

Mass losses of 3 to 14, 21 to 25, 33, 37, and 38 are highly unlikely (common neutral fragments lost are shown in Table A-5
and discussed in Chapter 6). If the elemental composition of
the fragment lost can be deduced, this gives an even more powerful test. For example, the presence of a major $(M - 15)^+$ ion is
common but a major $(M - NH)^+$ is probably an anomalous ion.
Can the ion of highest mass be the molecular ion if the following
are the major ions of high mass in the spectrum?

Unknown 3.2. $C_{10}H_{15}O$, $C_{10}H_{14}O$, $C_9H_{12}O$, $C_{10}H_{13}$, $C_8H_{10}O$.

Unknown 3.3. C_9H_{12}, C_9H_{11}, C_9H_9, C_8H_9, C_8H_7, C_7H_7.

Identifying the molecular ion is an important key to Unknown
3.4.

Unknown 3.4

m/e	Relative abundance	m/e	Relative abundance
12	2.7	49	4.2
13	3.0	49.5	0.02
14	0.63	50	1.5
15	0.05	51	0.31
24	4.0	59	2.6
25	15.	60	24.
26	34.	61	100.
27	1.2	62	9.9
30	0.06	63	32.
30.5	0.19	64	0.67
31	0.32	70	0.09
31.5	0.06	72	0.07
35	7.0	74	0.02
36	1.9	95	3.0
37	2.3	96	67.
38	0.68	97	3.3
47	6.5	98	43.
47.5	0.22	99	1.2
48	5.9	100	7.0
48.5	0.19	101	0.40

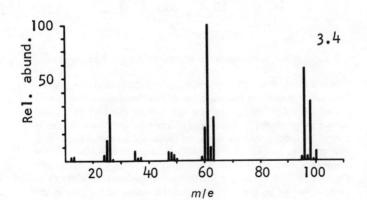

3.4

Unknown 3.5

m/e	Relative abundance	m/e	Relative abundance
31	42.	85	100.
32	0.50	86	1.1
35	2.5	87	33.
36	0.60	88	0.35
37	0.72	93	0.09
38	0.22	100	2.8
43	0.49	101	0.07
47	1.7	119	52.
49	0.57	120	1.2
50	11.	135	24.
51	0.13	136	0.52
62	0.19	137	7.7
69	57.	138	0.16
70	0.69		

3.5

3.3.   Other Techniques for Molecular Weight Determination

When identification of the molecular ion is doubtful or negative, there are a number of auxiliary techniques that can be valuable.

THE $(M + 1)^+$ ION.   Raising the sample pressure in the ion source increases the probability of reactions of the ions with sample molecules before removal from the reaction chamber. Such "ion-molecule reactions" (*3.5*) are bimolecular, so that the relative abundance of ions from such reactions increases with the sample pressure or with decreased ion-drawout (repeller) potential. (The latter is caused by the increased residence time of the ions in the ion source.)

A common ion-molecule reaction involves the abstraction of a hydrogen atom to form an ion of m/e that is one unit above the molecular weight, $(M + 1)^+$. It is fortunate that many types of compounds which give molecular ions of low abundance have a high cross section for such an ion-molecule reaction (3.6). Such compounds include aliphatic amines, alcohols, ethers, nitriles, sulfides, and similar compounds with heteroatom sites.

RATE OF EFFUSION. The sample flow rate out of the reservoir into the ion source is usually dependent on Graham's law of effusion. Thus the rate at which the sample pressure decreases is inversely proportional to the square root of the molecular weight of the compound. The measurement is most conveniently done by comparing the decay in the abundance of peaks from the unknown compound with time as compared to a reference compound measured simultaneously. The decay rate can be increased to a more convenient rate by using the small volume between the mass spectrometer isolation valve (if present) and the leak. Details of the technique are given in a number of references (1.1, 1.3, 1.11, 3.7). This has been used only to a limited extent because it often gives erroneous results. The chief causes of error are association to give higher molecular weight telomers, and adsorption. For nonpolar compounds, good accuracy can often be obtained.

LOW ENERGY ELECTRON BOMBARDMENT. Because the molecular ion is the precursor of all the other ions in the spectrum, it requires the least energy for its formation. Therefore, if the energy of the electron beam is lowered, the M^+ ion should be the last one to disappear. With oscilloscopic or other fast-scanning techniques, this is a relatively simple test for the peak at highest mass. If this peak is of low relative abundance at 70 eV, however, the test may be inconclusive. Of course the fact that a particular ion has the lowest appearance potential of any in the spectrum does not prove that this is a molecular ion—only the converse is true.

FIELD IONIZATION. The technique of "field ionization" can produce molecular ions from compounds for which the electron impact spectra show no appreciable M^+. In this technique, ionization is effected in a high field gradient between a sharp tip or edge and the entrance slit into the mass spectrometer. Apparently ionization does not take place through the usual Franck–Condon transition, but by a "tunneling" process so that the molecular ion can be formed in a lower energy state. For many compounds the field ion spectrum consists mainly of the molecular ion. There is a great deal of interest and progress in this field currently (3.8, 3.9), and commercial instruments have been announced recently which will permit a field ion spectrum to be recorded after the regular electron impact spectrum on a particular sample. Little information has been published, however, on higher molecular weight compounds.

In the following unknowns, you will probably not be able to assign complete structures for all of the spectra. You will find some of the minor ions of the spectra do not correspond to the arrangement of atoms in the original structure. These have been formed by rearrangement reactions, which will be discussed later in the text.

Unknown 3.6

m/e	Relative abundance	m/e	Relative abundance
12	1.9	42	1.5
13	3.4	43	3.1
14	8.3	44	4.7
15	51.	45	6.2
16	5.6	46	35.
26	1.6	47	0.17
27	6.9	48	0.15
28	6.3	59	0.06
29	8.0	60	4.0
30	100.	61	53.
31	1.4	62	1.0
32	0.53	63	0.22

Unknown 3.7

m/e	Relative abundance	m/e	Relative abundance
15	6.3	43	1.6
16	0.20	44	0.05
26	1.4	51	1.0
27	15.	52	0.27
28	2.4	53	1.2
29	38.	54	0.20
29.5	0.49	55	2.8
30	0.85	56	4.3
38	1.4	57	100.
39	13.	58	4.4
40	1.4	59	0.08
41	41.	71	0.04
42	2.3	72	0.01

Unknown 3.8

m/e	Relative abundance	m/e	Relative abundance
12	0.8	37	0.50
13	1.0	44	5.1
14	3.9	45	21.
15	4.6	46	14.
16	0.80	47	76.
26	17.	48	2.9
27	66.	49	3.4
28	51.	56	1.1
29	84.	57	6.0
30	2.0	58	8.6
31	0.02	59	6.5
32	6.4	60	1.2
33	8.3	61	13.
34	21.	62	100.
35	12.	63	3.6
36	1.0	64	4.4

Unknown 3.9

m/e	Relative abundance	m/e	Relative abundance
35	41.	72	0.92
36	0.71	74	0.16
37	13.	82	29.
38	0.23	83	0.77
41	1.2	84	19.
42	0.80	85	0.46
43	0.15	86	2.9
47	40.	87	0.07
48	0.49	117	100.
49	13.	118	0.57
50	0.16	119	96.
58.5	4.7	120	0.46
59.5	4.5	121	30.
60.5	1.4	122	0.11
61.5	0.16	123	3.1
70	1.4		

4

GENERAL APPEARANCE OF
THE SPECTRUM

If the nature of the sample is completely unknown, the overall appearance of the spectrum can often give a general indication of the type of compound. For this, the bar graph presentation is especially valuable. When studying instead the original spectrum (as recorded by the mass spectrometer), keep in mind the relative sensitivities of recording. Many instruments record using four or five simultaneous galvanometers with varying sensitivities, such as shown in Figure 1-2 or 2-2. The least sensitive galvanometer (Figure 1-1, for example) will usually resemble the bar graph presentation. The general appearance of the spectrum can indicate a number of pertinent points, as discussed in the following sections.

4.1.   Relative Stability of the Molecular Ion

In general, the abundance of the molecular ion is reflected by the chemical stability of the molecule. For example, the M^+ of paraffinic hydrocarbons is very low in abundance, while the molecular ion peak usually represents the majority of the ions found in the spectrum of a fused ring aromatic compound. Table A-3 indicates the molecular ion abundances found for a number of types of compounds, listed in order of generally decreasing abundance.

The molecular ion abundance generally increases with increased unsaturation and number of rings. For an element Y, the strength of the carbon-to-Y bond generally decreases in going down a column of the periodic table, as from Y = fluorine to iodine, but the effect of this on the molecular ion abundance is usually more than offset by an increased capacity to carry the positive charge on the Y atom; for example, the molecular ions of mercaptans and thioethers are generally more abundant than those of alcohols and ethers. Such polarizability effects parallel those leading to the high nucleophilicity of RS^- and I^- anions in solution displacement reactions. This tendency for increased M^+ abundance may also be partly due to lowering of particular driving forces for major decomposition reactions, such as lowering of the effectiveness of the heteroatom as a Lewis base.

One of the basic generalizations in use for years has been that the abundance of the molecular ion generally decreases with increasing molecular weight. Although this is valid and useful in increasing chain lengths up to C_6 or C_8, many exceptions have been found at higher molecular weights (see Table A-3). A better generalization may well be that M^+ abundances go through a minimum, then rise again. At higher molecular weights there may be increased opportunity for charge stabilization through cyclized ions or other structures affording greater charge delocalization. Of course the effect will depend on what structural moieties are used to increase the molecular weight; just increasing the length of the carbon chain apparently does not decrease (M^+) to the extent previously assumed. Most of the reference spectra of hydrocarbons (*1.17*) were recorded on Dempster 180°-type instruments, which discriminate against ions of higher mass. Also the temperature of the ion source appears to have a pronounced effect on the abundance of some molecular ions.

4.2. Relative Stability of Bonds

The number of abundant ions in the spectrum and their general distribution are also indicative of the type of molecule and the functional groups present. Unknown 4.1 has major fragment ions in a random type of distribution typical of this particular type of compound.

You should be able to recognize that the compound has the probable elemental composition $C_{16}H_{34}$, and that all of the major fragment ions are even-electron. The compound is *n*-hexadecane; the general appearance of the spectrum is typical of a straight-chain hydrocarbon. The regular distribution of the ions results from the fact that most of the carbon-carbon bonds are of nearly the same energy, as are the carbon-hydrogen bonds. Thus, the rates of the initial decomposition reactions of the molecular ion involving cleavages of the different carbon-carbon bonds are comparable to each other, as are the secondary decompositions of the primary product ions. This predicts a regular increase in abundances with decreased sizes of the alkyl ions. The possibility of rearranged products of greater stability becomes higher with the secondary reactions, so that the structures of the smaller ions, such as $C_3H_7^+$ and $C_4H_9^+$, are largely the more stable branched or possibly nonclassical (*4.1*) carbonium ion structures. Thus decomposition of the smaller fragment ions is generally slower than the larger, more highly linear species, and the distribution of ions is maximized in the C_3 and C_4 region of *n*-hexadecane (Unknown 4.1). What structure is indicated by the spectrum of Unknown 4.2?

Despite the fact that the molecular weight has more than doubled, distribution of ions remains qualitatively the same. The maximum in ion intensity is at a slightly higher carbon number, probably because of the increased opportunity for rearrangement in the secondary ions, and thus their increased stability.

The appearance of the *n*-paraffin spectrum serves as a key base point for recognition of compound types. Thus although chain branching of any kind in an aliphatic hydrocarbon will

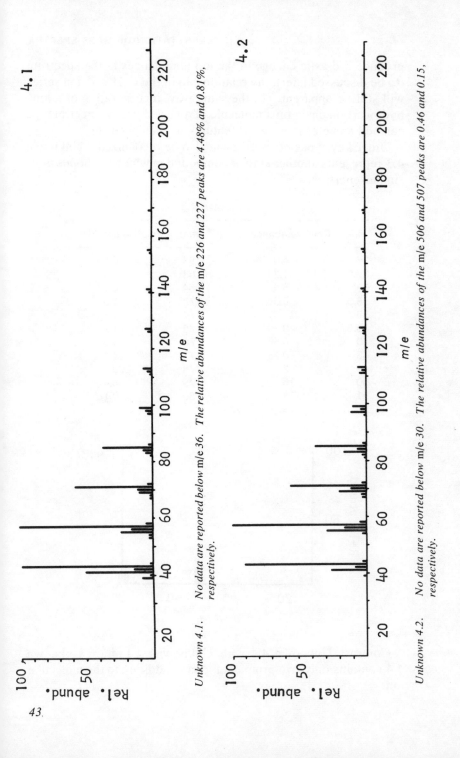

4.1

Unknown 4.1.   *No data are reported below m/e 36.   The relative abundances of the m/e 226 and 227 peaks are 4.48% and 0.81%, respectively.*

4.2

Unknown 4.2.   *No data are reported below m/e 30.   The relative abundances of the m/e 506 and 507 peaks are 0.46 and 0.15, respectively.*

produce a drastic change in the ion abundances in the spectrum (to be discussed later), the relationship in the $C_nH_{2n+1}^+$ ion series will still be apparent. In the same way, incorporation of a long hydrocarbon chain on a molecule of a very different spectral type can add some of these alkyl features to the spectrum.

Other key types of spectra can also be recognized. Unknown 4.3 represents another kind of compound in which the bonds have similar energies.

Unknown 4.3

m/e	Relative abundance	m/e	Relative abundance
37	4.0	53	0.80
37.5	1.2	63	2.9
38	5.4	64	0.17
38.5	0.35	73	1.5
39	13.	74	4.3
39.5	0.19	75	1.7
40	0.37	76	6.0
48	0.29	77	14.
49	2.7	78	100.
50	16.	79	6.4
51	18.	80	0.18
52	19.		

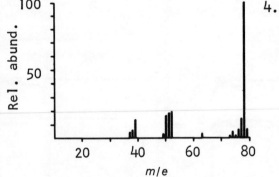

Contrast Unknown 4.4 with Unknowns 4.1–4.3. Unknown 4.4 contains only two prominent ions in addition to the molecular ion.

Unknown 4.4

m/e	Relative abundance	m/e	Relative abundance	m/e	Relative abundance	m/e	Relative abundance
27	1.3	74	2.0	105	100	153	1.8
28	1.0	75	1.7	106	7.8	154	1.4
38	0.37	75.5	0.21	107	0.51	155	0.16
39	1.1	76	4.3	119	0.02	164	0.06
50	6.2	76.5	0.33	126	0.63	165	0.44
51	19.	77	62.	127	0.40	166	0.06
52	1.4	78	4.2	128	0.13	181	8.2
53	0.29	79	0.16	139	0.17	182	60.
63	1.3	91	0.08	151	1.1	183	8.5
64	0.61	104	0.48	152	3.4	184	0.71
65	0.09						

4.4

m/e

A few prominent ions generally mean that there are only a few favored decomposition pathways. This is usually caused by the lability of one or a few bonds compared to the rest in the molecule, and (or) the stability of one or a few products compared with the other possibilities (this will be discussed in detail later).

In the spectrum of Unknown 4.5 the m/e 43 peak is by far the most prominent in the spectrum. The bond that is cleaved in the formation of this ion would be expected to be the weakest in the molecule from its known chemical reactivity.

Unknown 4.5

m/e	Relative abundance	m/e	Relative abundance
13	3.2	43	100.
14	10.	44	2.4
15	34.	45	0.31
16	0.55	56	0.26
26	2.0	57	0.10
27	1.4	71	0.01
28	1.0	86	11.
29	2.0	87	0.47
41	1.8	88	0.06
42	7.2		

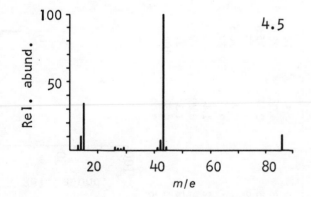

4.3. Greater Importance of Peaks at Higher Masses

In the n-hydrocarbon spectra discussed in Section 4.2, the presence of a $C_4H_9^+$ ion as the most abundant in the spectrum did not indicate that the bond between the fourth and fifth carbon atoms of the chain was the most labile. These ions were mainly formed through reaction pathways involving a number of successive decompositions, increasing the possibility of rearrangement. The structures of such ions and the pathways by which they are formed in a complex molecule are not well understood. It is empirically true, however, *that abundant ions at the low mass end of the spectrum are much less indicative of the molecular arrangement of the atoms than are ions at the high mass end of the spectrum,* even if the latter are much less abundant. In Unknown 4.6, one might arrive at the correct structure by use of the higher mass peaks only, but would have to eliminate the correct structure from consideration to account strictly for some of the low mass ions. The mechanisms of fragment ion formation for such compounds will be discussed later.

The size and nature of the group can drastically affect the degree of structural randomization at lower masses, however. The loss of an iodine atom from the molecular ion usually yields an ion of considerable structural significance, yet the m/e drops by 127 units. The largest peak in the spectra of n-alkylamines up to C_{15} is at m/e 30 ($CH_2NH_2^+$) because of the high stability of this ion, and it is thus very useful for structure determination. Knowledge of the elemental composition is obviously important for such cases. Further examples and the discussion of mechanisms later is the book should help clarify this.

The structural significance of relative ion abundances also increases with increasing mass of the ion. If the highest-mass peak is at m/e 172, a m/e 143 peak of 5% relative abundance is probably quite significant, but a 5% peak at m/e 43 is not. As a general rule of thumb to judge the relative importance of ion abundance at a particular mass, use the ion distribution of the n-paraffin spectra, for example, Unknowns 4.1 and 4.2. Thus the n-alkane of molecular weight near 172, $C_{12}H_{26}$, gives no peaks

Unknown 4.6

m/e	Relative abundance	m/e	Relative abundance
15	5.6	56	26.
26	0.43	57	100,
27	8.3	58	4.3
28	1.6	59	0.06
29	16.	69	1.4
30	0.31	70	0.12
39	8.5	71	0.33
40	1.4	72	0.03
41	27.	83	0.77
42	1.5	84	0.33
43	17.	85	0.03
44	0.60	98	0.04
45	0.03	99	6.1
53	1.3	100	0.47
54	0.28	101	0.03
55	4.1	114	0.02

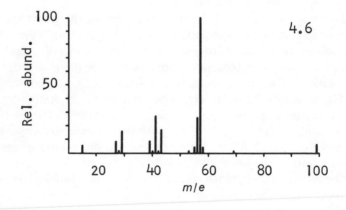

over 1% relative abundance around mass 143, while its *m/e* 43 peak is the largest in the spectrum. This indicates that the compound with the 5% 143 peak contains a structural grouping that can eject a 29 mass unit fragment (or fragments) more readily than the *n*-alkane losses $C_2H_5\cdot$. The 5% *m/e* 43 indicates, conversely, that $C_3H_7^+$ formation is of little importance.

4.4. Structural Significance of Ion Abundance

As we have just illustrated, the relative importance that should be attached to peak heights is a pitfall for the novice in mass spectrometry, as in most spectroscopic methods (except nuclear magnetic resonance). The chemical nature of the particular ion affects the significance of its abundance. The peak height should be compared to those of neighboring ions — those near in mass or in a homologous series. For several ions differing only in the number of hydrogen atoms, many of the ions of lower mass may have been formed from the one with the most hydrogen atoms. Thus an ion of m/e 141 is much more significant if the m/e 142 or 143, or the m/e 127 or 155, ions are of considerably lower abundance.

4.5. Multiply Charged Ions

In general, little use is made of doubly charged (or multiply charged) ions for structure determination. Few studies have been directed to this problem. Probably the most useful generalization is that abundant (a few per cent or more of the base peak) doubly charged ions are only found for highly stabilized molecules, such as fused-ring aromatics. Multiply charged ions are also abundant for some organometallic compounds and metals (such as Hg vapor). With an ionic charge (e) of 2, odd-numbered ion masses (m) will appear at fractional m/e (ending in .5), thus in most cases they are easily discernible in the spectrum. What doubly charged ions can you identify in Figure 2-2? Note that the most abundant doubly charged ions do *not* necessarily correspond in formula to the major singly charged ions.

For the Unknowns 4.7–4.10, the general appearance of the spectrum should give some indication of the structural type. If there does not appear to be enough information to make an absolute identification, record the possible molecular structures. Again there may be some misleading rearrangement ions present in the spectrum which have not as yet been explained in the text.

Unknown 4.7

m/e	Relative abundance	m/e	Relative abundance
12	2.4	92	6.1
13	4.7	93	100.
14	9.2	94	7.1
15	0.12	95	86.
39.5	0.65	96	1.0
40	0.07	158	1.5
40.5	0.64	159	0.03
41	0.06	160	2.9
79	22.	161	0.07
80	2.4	162	1.4
81	22.	163	0.03
82	2.3	170	0.37
85	0.24	171	0.63
85.5	0.08	172	51.
86	1.0	173	1.7
86.5	0.16	174	98.
87	1.4	175	1.5
87.5	0.08	176	48.
88	0.65	177	0.54
91	14.		

Unknown 4.8

m/e	Relative abundance	m/e	Relative abundance
14	1.3	33	32.
15	9.4	34	0.39
16	0.27	35	0.05
17	0.30	42	2.8
17.5	0.11	43	9.4
18	1.0	44	2.4
19	1.9	45	3.2
26	1.3	46	0.05
27	4.0	59	0.5
28	5.3	60	0.15
29	14.	61	1.3
30	2.0	62	3.1
31	100.	63	0.09
32	10.		

Unknowns 4.9 and 4.10

m/e	Relative abundance 4.9	4.10
12	3.6	0.98
13	3.0	1.2
14	4.9	1.8
15	3.3	0.50
24	1.1	0.18
25	3.4	1.0
26	13.	3.3
27	37.	2.6
28	7.8	42.
29	0.29	0.74
30	0.02	0.12
31.5	0.40	—
32	0.75	—
32.5	1.5	1.6
33	0.11	0.20
33.5	—	7.7
34	—	0.35
36	4.1	1.5
37	16.	11.6
38	20.	19.
39	44.	57.
40	25.	50.
41	100.	58.
42	2.7	1.5
43	0.23	0.12
50	2.0	0.73
51	3.2	0.71
52	8.1	2.0
53	0.31	0.12
62	1.3	0.44
63	3.0	0.87
64	6.7	1.0
65	1.7	0.88
66	11.	6.9
67	34.	100.
68	1.6	4.7
69	0.06	0.12

5

SERIES OF EVEN-ELECTRON IONS

Despite the lesser structural significance of the low mass ions, the more detailed study of the spectrum should start at the low mass end. Both the isobaric and isomeric structural possibilities for ions at a particular mass increase exponentially with m/e. CH_3^+ is the main cause found for a sizable m/e 15 peak, while both $C_2H_5^+$ and CHO^+ are common at m/e 29, and a number of ions besides $C_3H_7^+$ can cause an abundant m/e 43. Identifications are also simpler at the low mass end because the abundant low mass ions are usually even-electron. The structural implications of these ions can often indicate the most probable of the isomeric and isobaric possibilities for the high mass ions when the latter are studied.

5.1. Series Separated by CH_2 Groups

Many structural features give rise to a significant homologous series of ions starting at the low mass end of the spectrum, such as the continuous series of alkyl ions, $C_nH_{2n+1}^+$, in n-paraffin spectra (see Unknowns 4.1 and 4.2). The high probability of rearrangement on forming the lowest mass ions produces a much more complete homologous series with much less variation in ion abundances than at higher masses. The hydrocarbon $(CH_3)_3CC(CH_3)_3$ (Unknown 4.6) does not contain a C_2H_5 or C_3H_7 grouping, yet it gives the ion series CH_3^+, 5.6%; $C_2H_5^+$, 16%; $C_3H_7^+$, 17%; and $C_4H_9^+$, 100%. Thus a quick inspection of the spectrum starting at the low mass end of Unknown 4.6 indicates the presence of an alkyl moiety. The fact that the $C_nH_{2n+1}^+$ ions can be traced from CH_3^+ to $C_7H_{15}^+$ is a valuable indication (although not a proof) of the size of the alkyl moiety.

A substituted alkyl group will produce a homologous series of displaced mass, for example, amines, 30, 44, 58, . . . ; alcohols, 31, 45, 59, . . . ; ketones, 43, 57, 71, . . . (unfortunately —CO— corresponds to —C_2H_4— in mass, causing overlap with the alkyl series); and chloroalkanes, 49, 63, 77, ... A variety of such ion series is listed in Table A-4, along with the most probable types of molecular structures in whose spectra they are found. These are made up mainly of even-electron ions because of their generally greater stability. Note that many of the common series can be confused by the possibility of isobaric multiplets, so that the accurate determination of elemental composition greatly improves the usefulness of this table.

> Most of the series shown involve ions separated by —CH_2— groups, but many other series are indicative for other types of compounds such as polyunsaturated, polycyclic, and polysubstituted compounds. Such series will be discussed later in the chapter. The "shift technique," which can be viewed as a specific extension of this principle, will be discussed in Section 9.1.

Unknown 5.1 is made difficult by the fact that the relative abundances of the peaks at highest mass are insufficient for an accurate determination of elemental composition. The possibilities for this, however, are narrowed rapidly with the assignment of the low mass ions to a logical even-electron series.

Unknown 5.1

m/e	Relative abundance	m/e	Relative abundance
15	7.2	70	7.8
27	19.	71	13.
28	3.1	72	0.73
29	34.	73	0.02
30	0.74	83	0.45
39	10.	84	0.11
40	1.5	85	0.36
41	31.	86	0.02
42	5.7	97	0.13
43	32.	98	3.7
44	1.0	99	10.
45	0.03	100	0.77
53	2.0	101	0.04
54	0.56	112	0.06
55	9.9	113	0.32
56	15.	114	0.03
57	100.	127	0.04
58	4.3	128	0.65
59	0.08	129	0.05
69	2.7		

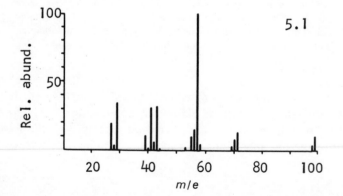

The solution of Unknown 5.2, which also has a molecular weight of 128, is indicated by the elemental composition and the high abundance of the molecular ion. Note, however, the striking differences between the spectra in the masses of ions in the lower end of the spectrum.

Unknown 5.2

m/e	Relative abundance	m/e	Relative abundance
38	1.8	64.5	1.1
39	3.9	65	0.24
40	0.19	66	0.02
41	0.01	74	4.7
42	0.06	75	4.9
42.67	0.10	76	3.3
43	0.16	77	4.1
43.5	0.02	78	2.7
49.5	0.24	79	0.19
50	6.4	87	1.4
50.5	0.09	88	0.22
51	12.	89	0.73
51.5	0.37	90	0.06
52	1.6	101	2.7
53	0.27	102	7.1
54	0.04	103	0.64
55	0.14	104	0.15
55.5	0.03	110	0.06
56	0.12	111	0.09
56.5	0.06	112	0.02
61	1.4	113	0.18
61.5	0.08	125	0.85
62	2.7	126	6.1
62.5	0.20	127	9.8
63	7.4	128	100.
63.5	0.95	129	11.
64	10.	130	0.41

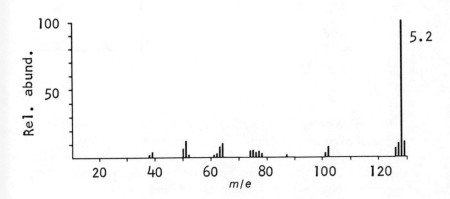

In Unknown 5.3 the use of Table A-4 should clear up any confusion about the identity of the molecular ion. In Unknown 5.4, however, the search for an even-electron ion series could lead to quite different conclusions.

Unknowns 5.3 and 5.4

m/e	Relative abundance	
	5.3	5.4
15	2.8	3.2
16	0.03	1.1
26	1.4	0.52
27	10.	2.7
28	5.2	4.4
29	6.0	2.3
30	0.33	100.
31	4.5	1.9
37	1.2	0.09
38	1.9	0.33
39	5.8	0.57
40	1.0	1.0
41	7.2	2.5
42	4.2	5.4
43	19.	7.1
44	3.9	3.7
45	100.	0.09
46	2.5	—
47	0.19	—
57	0.41	0.27
58	0.20	0.60
59	4.3	3.6
60	0.51	5.2
61	0.03	0.17

For more complex molecules, there may well be a number of series of even-electron ions. Try to account for all major even-electron ions in the lower half of the mass spectrum. Following the series does not have to be limited to the lower half of the spectrum, however; in Unknowns 4.6 and 5.1 the alkyl series

C_nH_{2n+1} can be carried nearly all the way to the molecular ion. Note also that attempts to continue the series should not be abandoned if the next higher member happens to be of low abundance. As stated previously, the significance of the relative abundance (both low and high abundance) of individual ions becomes much greater towards the high mass end of the spectrum.

A common decomposition of even-electron ions is the loss of a small molecule. Thus a peak of fair abundance may appear two mass units below an abundant even-electron ion through the loss of a hydrogen molecule, and cause another homologous series of even-electron ions whose structural significance could be confusing. In Unknown 5.1 the C_nH_{2n-1} series of fair abundance does *not* indicate the presence of olefinic or cycloalkyl structures as might be deduced from Table A-4. Note, however, that a multiply unsaturated or cyclic molecule, as C_nH_{2n-4}, will also give even-electron ions that are *less* hydrogen-deficient. Thus cyclohexene, C_6H_{10}, gives the ion series CH_3^+, $C_2H_5^+$, $C_3H_7^+$ (rearrangements) and $C_2H_3^+$, $C_3H_5^+$, $C_4H_7^+$, in addition to the expected C_2H^+ (small), $C_3H_3^+$, $C_4H_5^+$, $C_5H_7^+$, $C_6H_9^+$. In the absence of rearrangements, the size of the $C_nH_{2n-3}^+$, $C_nH_{2n-1}^+$, and $C_nH_{2n+1}^+$ ions can then indicate the location of the unsaturation and (or) rings in the molecule.

5.2.   Other Ion Series

Compounds with a low hydrogen-to-carbon ratio, such as Unknowns 4.3 and 5.2, do not have sufficient hydrogen atoms for such a series of ions spaced at 14 mass unit intervals. In aromatic hydrocarbons the fragment ions 39, 50, 51, 52, 63, 64, 65, 75, 76, 77 (roughly $C_nH_{0.5n}$ to C_nH_n) are typical (Table A-4). Heterocyclic compounds containing ring oxygen and nitrogen atoms show similar m/e fragments plus additional significant peaks at masses 40, 53, 66, and 78 due to replacement of C by N or O.

The substitution of hydrogen atoms by halogen atoms, X, changes the homologous series spacings by CHX or CX_2, causing a marked change in the appearance of the spectrum. Additionally, the electronegative halogen atoms are much more easily lost than hydrogen atoms, so that ions separated by X and HX in mass are also found. For chlorine and bromine, these are easily identified because of the "isotope clusters" (Section 2.3) produced by the abundant natural isotopes of Cl and Br. Fluorine and iodine each have only one natural isotope, F^{19} and I^{127}, but these can usually be recognized by the very unusual mass differences they cause.

> Inclusion of halogen atoms increases the masses substantially, so that the definition of a "low mass ion series" must be viewed in an expanded dimension. Thus although the spectrum of $n\text{-}C_4F_{10}$ shows a series $C_nF_{2n+1}{}^+$ in the same way that $n\text{-}C_4H_{10}$ shows the series $C_nH_{2n+1}{}^+$ in Unknown 2.3, the former ion series is 69, 119, 169, and 219 in contrast to the familiar alkyl series of the latter of 15, 29, 43, and 57.

Although Unknowns 5.5 through 5.8 were chosen to illustrate the usefulness of low mass even-electron ion series, be sure to follow all the preliminary steps of the standard interpretation procedure, Table A-1.

Unknown 5.5

m/e	Relative abundance	m/e	Relative abundance	m/e	Relative abundance	m/e	Relative abundance
38	0.16	75.5	0.43	102	1.0	154	0.04
39	1.0	76	10.	103	1.1	163	0.70
40	0.05	76.5	1.3	115	0.54	164	0.20
50	1.0	77	1.1	126	2.7	165	0.68
51	2.3	78	0.22	127	0.89	166	0.07
52	0.67	87	1.3	128	0.64	174	0.53
53	0.06	87.5	0.19	129	0.08	175	2.3
63	3.6	88	3.6	139	2.3	176	14.
63.5	0.19	88.5	0.62	140	0.41	177	10.
64	0.38	89	7.4	150	3.9	178	100.
65	0.41	89.5	1.4	151	7.9	179	15.4
74	1.8	90	0.21	152	8.4	180	1.1
75	2.4	91	0.13	153	1.0		

5.5

Unknown 5.6

m/e	Relative abundance	m/e	Relative abundance
12	13.	50	25.
14	2.1	51	0.31
19	2.0	69	100.
24	2.7	70	1.08
26	11.	76	46.
27	0.11	77	1.0
31	22.	95	2.4
32	0.28	96	0.06
38	6.2		

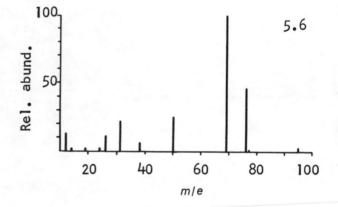

Unknown 5.7

m/e	Relative abundance	m/e	Relative abundance
37	2.7	65	0.80
37.5	0.12	65.5	0.05
38	3.7	73	1.0
38.5	0.05	74	7.1
39	4.8	75	9.9
40	0.62	76	9.0
40.5	0.10	77	3.8
41	0.38	78	2.5
42	0.11	79	0.45
43	0.48	80	0.20
43.5	0.03	81	0.42
44	1.6	86	0.42
44.5	0.02	87	0.94
45	0.10	88	0.35
49	2.0	89	0.26
49.5	0.64	90	0.16
50	12.	97	0.33
50.5	0.47	98	1.2
51	19.	99	0.91
51.5	1.0	100	0.94
52	4.2	101	5.6
53	0.41	102	24.
61	1.8	103	7.6
61.5	0.07	104	0.62
62	3.2	126	0.15
62.5	0.07	127	1.8
63	5.8	128	16.
63.5	0.14	129	100.
64	1.5	130	10.
64.5	3.9	131	0.56

Unknown 5.8

m/e	Relative abundance	m/e	Relative abundance	m/e	Relative abundance	m/e	Relative abundance
15	0.66	56	17.	91	0.15	122	0.05
26	1.3	57	21.	92	0.04	123	0.40
27	18.	58	0.96	93	1.2	133	0.04
28	3.5	69	6.0	94	0.05	134	0.04
29	18.	70	0.53	95	1.2	135	50.
39	11.	71	0.53	105	0.28	136	2.2
40	2.1	79	0.19	106	0.64	137	49.
41	37.	80	0.10	107	5.0	138	2.1
42	14.	81	0.19	108	0.73	139	0.05
43	100.	82	0.13	109	4.7	164	2.2
44	3.4	83	0.74	110	0.14	165	0.15
53	2.1	84	0.66	119	0.25	166	2.2
54	1.1	85	49.	120	0.05	167	0.13
55	34.	86	3.2	121	0.56		

5.8

6

IDENTIFICATION OF NEUTRAL
FRAGMENTS

Perhaps the most simple and positive assignments that can be made in the spectrum are for the small neutral species lost in the formation of the fragment ions of highest masses in the spectrum, especially those formed directly from the molecular ion. For example, the ions at masses $(M - 1)^+$, $(M - 15)^+$, $(M - 18)^+$, and $(M - 20)^+$ almost always represent the losses of H, CH_3, H_2O, and HF, respectively, from the molecular ion. Because formation of such large primary ions involves the lowest probability of a randomizing rearrangement, such neutral fragment losses are of major significance in determining the molecular structure. Thus an abundant peak corresponding to $(M - 1)^+$ indicates a labile hydrogen atom (and the absence of other labile substituents), and an abundant peak corresponding to $(M - 15)^+$ indicates a methyl group on a substituted carbon or similar position from which it can be readily lost.

If it has been possible to assign elemental compositions to the decomposing and product ion of a particular reaction, then the neutral fragment composition is obvious by difference. If the elemental composition assignments for the ions are in doubt, a low mass neutral product may often help clarify these because of the unique or limited formulas possible for it. Consider an unknown having a m/e 74 molecular ion whose elemental composition is in doubt because of its low abundance. A major ion at m/e 59 has the composition $C_2H_3O_2^+$. Because the neutral fragment lost almost surely is CH_3, the elemental composition of the molecular ion is obvious.

As the neutral fragments increase in mass, the isobaric or isomeric possibilities cause an increasing probability of confusion in assignments. It also becomes more difficult to determine from which particular ion the fragment ion in question is formed. For example, in a spectrum containing abundant $(M - CH_3)^+$ and $(M - C_3H_7)^+$ ions, the latter could be formed either by the loss of the propyl radical as nominally indicated, or by the loss of an ethylene molecule from the $(M - CH_3)^+$ ion. A list of common neutral fragments lost in the formation of major ions is set forth in Table A-5.

6.1.   Metastable Ion Decompositions

A metastable ion is one that decomposes after nearly complete acceleration from the ion source but before complete mass analysis (lifetime of roughly 10^{-6} second). The product ion from such a decomposition gives rise to a somewhat diffuse peak in the spectrum below its actual m/e, called a "metastable peak," "metastable ion," or just a "metastable" by most mass spectrometrists. (To be exact, this terminology is erroneous, as such a peak represents the *product* of the decomposition of a metastable ion. Quotation marks will be used to make this differentiation.) Acceleration of the ion to a velocity determined by the higher mass followed by magnetic deflection at the lower mass results in collection at a still lower m/e, with kinetic energies of decomposition and variation of lifetimes causing a broad distribution of the m/e of focus.

Such "metastables" are quite useful in elucidating ion decomposition pathways, despite the fact that they only represent the slowest of the 10^{-14} to 10^{-6} second reaction times which form the ions seen in the mass spectrum. Identification of a particular reaction pathway can provide valuable evidence as to the arrangement of atoms in a molecule. For example, in a hypothetical spectrum the presence of ions corresponding in mass to AB and ABC could indicate either of the molecular structure possibilities A-B-C-B-A or A-B-B-C-A. However, a metastable decomposition of ABC → AB would be possible, barring rearrangements, only for the structure A-B-C-B-A. Thus for A-B-B-C-A the "metastable" shows that the part of the molecule that contains A, B and C does not have A adjacent to B.

In general, although not always, the precursor and daughter ions of such a metastable ion decomposition are also of significance at their true m/e in the spectrum. It is important to note, however, that many reactions producing major ions are *not* represented by such "metastable" peaks in the spectrum. Also, the presence of a peak representing a metastable ion decomposition to form a particular fragment ion only shows that *some* of the normal peak for this ion in the spectrum is formed by this particular pathway, not necessarily *all*. There may be alternative pathways to the same fragment ion.

In the conventional single-focusing magnetic mass spectrometer the product ion, m_2, from the decomposition of a precursor ion, m_1, is most likely to be found at a mass m^*, where $m^* = m_2^2/m_1$. Thus m^* should be the m/e of the center of the roughly Gaussian distribution of ions of the "metastable" peak. Figure 6-1 is a recorder trace of a mass spectrum which shows a number of "metastables." Pick these out.

One method of recording the large possible range of relative ion abundances that can be detected (a factor of up to 10^7, with electron multipliers) is to use a logarithmic recorder (*6.1*). As recently pointed out (*6.2*), this display of the spectrum greatly simplifies identification of "metastables." Increasing the width of the collector slit will also accentuate the abundance of the "metastables," although this increases the width of ordinary peaks so that they interfere more with "metastable" identification. With double-focusing mass spectrometers of both the Nier–Johnson (*6.3, 6.4*) and the Mattauch–Herzog (*6.5, 6.6*) types the relative abundances of the "metastables" may be considerably enhanced by special techniques. For the time-of-flight mass spectrometer, the addition

of a retarding region in front of the collector (6.7) makes possible
detection of some metastable transitions that are difficult to observe
in magnetic instruments (6.8).

Obviously there are many combinations of precursor and
daughter ion masses which can yield a "metastable" peak at a
particular mass. The usual approach for assigning the most
probable decomposition reaction to a particular "metastable"
peak is the trial and error method, trying the major ions as both
precursors and daughters. This can be done with a slide rule
using the equation above, by using computer-calculated tables
of ion combinations (6.9), or a nomograph (1.1). Such a nomograph is shown in Table A-6. Its use can be illustrated by
application to the "metastables" tabulated from Figure 6-1.
Major ions of the spectrum are at m/e 58, 43, 42, 41, 39, 29, 28,
27. For the diffuse peak (m^*) at m/e 39.2, there are only four
major ions of higher mass to consider as either the m_1 or m_2 ions.
The first ion which might be tried as the m_1 is the m/e 58, but
obviously it is of much too high a mass compared to the others
(m_2 would then be 47.6). Trying the next major ion, m/e 43,
yields m/e 41 as the obvious choice for m_2. For Unknown 6.1,
continue this process for the other "metastable" peaks shown in
Figure 6-1. (Ignore the large air impurity.)

You may prefer to use the slide rule because of its convenience
and accuracy. Set the proper index of the "B" scale opposite
the m^* value on the "A" scale. Then setting the slide on the
"B" scale at the suspected m_1 value will give the corresponding
m_2 mass under the slide on the "D" scale.

The experienced interpreter usually does not bother to identify
each metastable transition of a mass spectrum. In line with
the previous discussion, the most important "metastables" are
those which indicate the pathways of decomposition and (or)
formation of the major ions of high mass in the spectrum. In
Unknown 6.1 the "metastable" at 39.2 signifies that the $C_3H_5^+$
ion is formed at least in part from the $C_3H_7^+$ ion, a fact hardly
necessary in the elucidation of this spectrum. In learning the
interpretation of spectra, it is recommended that a number of the
higher mass metastable transitions of each spectrum be identified.
This is relatively simple, and is probably the best way to learn

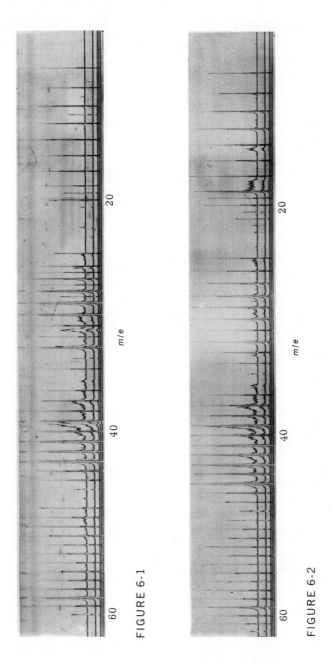

FIGURE 6-1

FIGURE 6-2

m/e

20

40

60

which "metastables" can be ignored safely. The size and shape of a "metastable" peak are related to its ion degradation process, although these relations are not thoroughly understood at present.

The actual spectrum recorded for Unknown 5.3 is shown in Figure 6-2. The presence of which particular "metastable" in the spectrum eliminates the molecule CH_3COOH from consideration? (The answer is given in Chapter 10 as that for Unknown 6.2.)

"Metastable" peak data were omitted from most previous unknowns to avoid confusion. When available such data will be included in the remainder of the unknowns.

6.2.   Odd-Electron Ion Formation

The formation of abundant odd-electron ions almost always occurs from the molecular ion or from another odd-electron ion, and thus this formation usually involves the loss of a molecule. For the formation of major odd-electron ions of high mass the moieties lost are typically small stable molecules, such as H_2, CH_4, H_2O, C_2H_4, NO, C_2H_2, and so on. Such losses are usually quite easily identified in the high mass end of the spectrum (see Table A-5). Mark these on the spectrum. As will be discussed later, these are often quite significant for elucidation of the spectrum.

6.3.   Even-Electron Ion Formation

The more abundant even-electron ions at high mass are formed by loss of a neutral radical from the molecular ion or other odd-electron ion, or by loss of a neutral molecule from another even-electron ion. Where possible, tentative assignments should again be made from the high mass ions with the help of Table A-5.

Although the structural significance of the fragment ions of Unknowns 6.3, 6.4, and 6.5 will be discussed more fully later, attempt solutions with the principles already covered.

Unknowns 6.3–6.5

m/e	Relative abundance		
	6.3	6.4	6.5
15	1.1	14.	21.
26	3.3	—	1.3
27	14.	—	0.4
28	11.	7.1	5.6
29	17.	63.	16.
30	2.2	6.9	0.69
31	100.	100.	4.5
32	2.3	34.	0.11
33	1.1	0.63	—
37	1.0	—	—
38	1.5	—	—
39	5.6	—	0.08
40	1.5	—	1.1
41	10.	0.12	3.7
42	13.	0.16	12.
43	3.8	0.23	100.
44	0.11	1.5	4.9
45	4.6	1.4	94.
46	0.12	—	1.2
47	—	—	0.40
57	2.9	—	—
58	5.0	—	—
59	15.	0.48	—
60	11.	28.	58.
61	0.38	0.70	1.4
62	0.03	0.13	0.26

7

POSTULATION OF ION STRUCTURES

Applying the instructions in Chapters 1 through 6 to an unknown mass spectrum will have led to structure postulations for a number of the ions in the spectrum. There are other such postulations that should be considered before attempting to use the collected information to formulate a structure for the molecule itself. To reiterate, while learning to interpret spectra it is important not to become impatient and jump ahead to this obvious and enticing last step before assembling these important individual pieces of data. For many of the spectra much of these data will not be necessary to reach the solution, and with experience, some of these preliminary steps can be omitted. However, with practice these steps take a relatively short time for the major ions of the average spectrum, and often yield clues that save a great deal of time with the final analysis.

This step of postulating structures of particular ions, or types of molecular functionality from which particular ions arise, is mainly based on experience as to what significance an ion of a particular m/e (or elemental composition) often has. Thus from experience in infrared spectroscopy or from a correlation table such as the "Colthup" chart (7.1), particular absorption bands signify particular functional groups. With no other knowledge of a sample, the experienced infrared interpreter would immediately suspect a carbonyl function such as an ester if he saw a band at 1740 cm^{-1}. In the same way an abundant peak at m/e 91 would lead the experienced mass spectrometrist to look for a benzyl moiety in the molecule; m/e 74, the methyl ester of a fatty acid; m/e 149, a phthalate ester; m/e 30, an amine, especially a primary amine; and m/e 124 in a plant extract sample, an aspidospermine or similar type of alkaloid. Such generalizations are usually a vital part in the elucidation of a spectrum. However, it should be borne in mind that these are only postulations—*few are infallible,* although many can give strong indications of structure. An abundant m/e 43 ion for which the elemental composition is unknown often signifies an acetyl or isopropyl group in the molecule, but can also arise from a cyclic hydrocarbon or even represent $C_2H_5N^+$ or $CHNO^+$. Where more than one possible interpretation exists, be sure to note all of them; then if other evidence in the spectrum eliminates one or more of these possibilities, the others will be much more meaningful.

There are two main problems for such postulations which are especially acute for the inexperienced: what elemental compositions and structures are possible for the peak, and what the *relative* probability is for each of these postulations. For these problems the author has a chauvinistic prejudice for the tabulations found in *Mass Spectral Correlations (1.15).* Its use is illustrated in Figure 7-1 by a copy of its data on the ions of m/e 43. This shows that mass 43 ions of elemental formulas CHNO, C_2H_3O, CH_3N_2, C_2H_5N, and C_3H_7 are all possible at mass 43. High resolution or other elemental composition information could distinguish these. Figure 7-1 also shows that ions of a particular formula can arise from a number of general types of compounds. Thus, the ion $C_2H_3O^+$ is abundant in the spectra of methyl ketones, acetates, and acetamides, and can even arise from compounds that do not bear the obvious

$$\underset{CH_3C-}{\overset{\displaystyle O}{\overset{\displaystyle \|}{}}}$$

group, such as vinyl and cyclic ethers. The table thus has a considerable value for the beginner in avoiding the quick con-

m/e	Formula	Structural Significance	Relative Probability			Total
			1	2	3	
43.0058	CHNO	R-O⊣CONH⊣H, R₂N⊣CONH⊣H(?)	4		1	5
43.0184	C_2H_3O	CH_3CO⊣R	30	4	14	48
		CH_3CO⊣OR	36	7	11	54
		CH_3CO⊣NR_2	2	5	17	24
		Cyclic ethers	4	11	4	19
		Other satd. ROH, ROR, mixed	5	7	15	27
		CH_2=CHO⊣R		2	3	5
		Other		1	2	3
43.0296	CH_3N_2	CH_3N=N⊣CH_3		1		1
43.0421	C_2H_5N	Cyclic amines	2			2
		Other	3			3
43.0547	C_3H_7	$(CH_3)_2$CH⊣C_nH_{2n+1}	29	8		37
		Other $(CH_3)_2$CH⊣R, $(CH_3)_2$CH⊣RY	31	20	20	71
		$CH_3CH_2CH_2$⊣CHRR', ⊣CRR'R" (branched)	9	3	1	13
		$CH_3CH_2CH_2$⊣R (R= -C-C≡C, -C-Ph)	2	1	1	4
		Other $CH_3CH_2CH_2$⊣ C_nH_{2n+1}	43	33	20	96
		Cpds. with large satd. h.c. groups	26	82	80	188
		C_3H_7-Y (Y= -COOR)	9	4		13
		(Y= -CONR₂)		1	1	2
		(Y= -COR)	5	1		6
		(Y= -NR₂)			1	1
		(Y= -SR or -SSR)	4		4	8
		(Y= -OR)	10	4	2	16
		(Y= -OCOR*)	4	5	3	12
		(Y= X)	5			5
		(Y= -NO₂)	2			2
		P.I.D. and unclassified	13	9	5	27
		Total	279	210	203	692

FIGURE 7-1

clusion that the presence of an abundant $C_2H_3O^+$ ion signifies an acetyl group in the molecule.

The relative probability of a particular structural significance for an ion is shown in the columns of numbers. The tabulation was prepared by the examination of the major peaks in the mass spectra of 4000 different compounds. In the column headed *1*, the figure shown signifies the number of times that an ion of this particular origin gives the largest peak in the spectrum. In the column headed *2*, the entry similarly signifies the number of times that the same ion was the second most abundant in the spectrum. Obviously, a molecule containing a number of functional groups or structural moieties would yield ions characteristic of each of these groups in competition, so that a distribution of entries in this column would be expected. Note also that the 4000 spectra examined for the study are a "random" sample only as far as the types of compounds examined by the author's laboratory are concerned. For the simplest molecular structures, most of the possible compounds are included, and therefore the figures for these are fairly representative.

Considering again the case of an unknown abundant peak of m/e 43, the most obvious way to classify it further is through information on its elemental composition. This may come from the spectrum (for example, isotopic peaks), other mass spectral measurements (such as high resolution), or outside information (such as elemental analysis). If the ion corresponds to $CHNO^+$, this would strongly suggest the grouping

in the molecule. If the ion is $C_2H_3O^+$ and the largest peak in the spectrum, the acetyl group would be likely. Other possibilities are listed, however, and these would be more probable if the $C_2H_3O^+$ were less prominent in the spectrum. It should be reemphasized that a positive identification or decision is neither necessary nor desirable at this point. This is best done by considering all of the available information together, as explained in Chapter 9. For example, the additional presence of a prominent $C_2H_5O_2^+$ peak in the spectrum would indicate that both it and the $C_2H_3O^+$ probably arose from an acetate ester grouping.

7.1. Odd-Electron Ions

Many abundant odd-electron ions are the result of "specific" rearrangements, making them indicative of one or a few possible structural types. A number of common odd-electron ions are tabulated in Table A-7. Although their significance will be much clearer after the discussion of such rearrangements in the next chapter, you should be able to solve Unknown 7.1 using the previous instruction and Table A-7.

Unknown 7.1

m/e	Relative abundance	m/e	Relative abundance
26	2.4	55	2.6
27	14.	56	8.9
28	4.3	57	27.
29	33.	58	1.3
30	0.75	59	0.08
31	0.26	71	0.87
39	7.7	72	17.
40	0.95	73	0.78
41	26.	74	0.06
42	3.8	85	2.3
43	100.	86	0.14
44	2.4	87	0.04
45	1.2	99	0.12
46	0.04	100	3.4
53	1.0	101	0.29
54	0.36	102	0.04

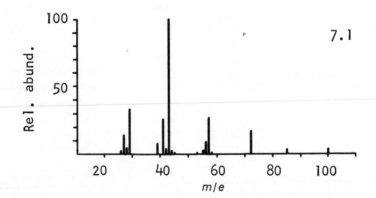

7.2. Even-Electron Ions

Check the major even-electron ions again to see if additional structures are possible for any of these (record all possibilities). Use evidence such as elemental composition, "rings plus double bonds," or "Mass Spectral Correlations." The more common possibilities are also shown in Table A-4. Your more extensive efforts to assign structures to individual ions, however, will naturally lead into the remaining parts of the elucidation of the spectrum, discussed in the last two chapters. Before studying these, try Unknowns 7.2, 7.3, and 7.4. Do these as a group to evaluate the usefulness of cross comparison of spectra.

Unknowns 7.2-7.4

m/e	Relative abundance			m/e	Relative abundance		
	7.2	7.3	7.4		7.2	7.3	7.4
39	8.9	3.9	8.5	74	1.2	4.4	0.60
40	0.79	0.25	0.71	75	1.3	2.2	0.56
41	4.4	0.24	3.3	76	1.0	3.7	0.47
42	0.38	0.99	0.21	77	13.	74.	3.2
43	1.4	15.	0.09	78	5.3	7.7	6.1
46.4 m	0.03	—	0.15	79	9.5	0.33	1.3
50	4.5	7.6	2.4	80	0.61	—	0.09
50.5	0.14	—	0.04	89	0.84	0.86	1.6
51	12.	22.	6.0	90	0.24	0.26	0.84
51.5	0.65	0.32	0.07	91	5.2	1.3	100.
52	3.3	2.6	1.6	92	0.69	0.07	10.
52.5	1.3	1.5	0.03	93	0.05	—	0.47
53	1.5	0.34	0.64	101.0 m	0.59	—	—
56.5 m	0.09	—	—	103	5.9	0.17	1.0
57	0.33	—	0.24	104	2.2	0.27	0.59
57.5	0.71	—	0.77	105	100.	100.	3.3
58	1.0	—	0.52	106	8.5	7.8	0.33
58.5	0.08	—	0.09	107	0.32	0.49	0.04
59	1.1	—	—	115	0.88	—	1.0
59.4 m	0.30	—	—	116	0.17	—	0.27
62	1.0	1.8	1.0	117	0.44	—	0.59
63	2.9	2.4	3.1	118	0.16	—	0.12
64	0.54	0.52	0.79	119	0.83	—	0.17
65	2.4	2.1	9.3	120	25.	28.	21.
66	0.29	0.08	0.61	121	2.4	2.5	2.0
69.0 m	0.02	—	0.13	122	0.10	0.18	0.09
73	0.16	0.91	0.09				

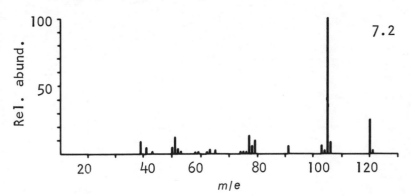

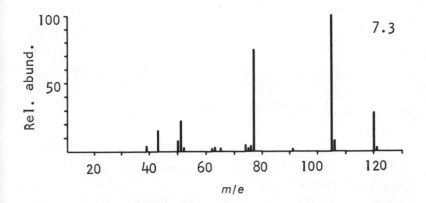

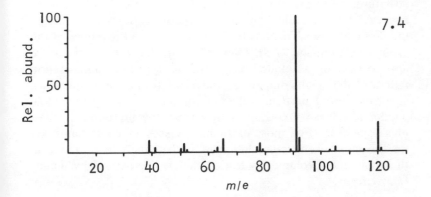

8

MECHANISMS OF UNIMOLECULAR
ION DECOMPOSITION REACTIONS

To assemble the variety and multiplicity of data in the mass spectrum into the most logical postulation for the molecular structure requires an understanding of the basic processes involved in forming mass spectra. Our present understanding is due largely to the study of mass spectra of compounds of known structure. For example, the mass spectrometer has been very successful in the elucidation of structures of many complex indole alkaloids. This has been largely due to the efforts of the groups of Biemann (*1.3*), Djerassi (*1.6*), and others who were able to develop a detailed picture of the types of fragmentation reactions that such compounds undergo. If one has an unknown spectrum from a particular class of compounds such as the indole alkaloids, a wise first step is to review the literature on their mass spectra. For most particular classes of compounds, by far the most useful compilation of such data is to be found in the three recent volumes by Budzikiewicz, Djerassi, and Williams (*1.5, 1.6*).

Such studies have led to generalizations concerning the common types of unimolecular ion decomposition reactions (*1.3, 1.11, 3.3, 8.1, 8.2, 8.5a*). In the following outline an effort has been made to classify common mechanisms for a wide variety of structural types into fewer, more basic, categories. Despite the danger of oversimplification, it is hoped that the student will find compensating efficiency in the learning process through postponing the consideration of exceptions until after simplified generalizations have been digested.

In the ion source the interaction of a 50–100 V electron with a molecule produces a molecular ion in an excited energy state. Although the bombarding electron energies are roughly 1000 kcal above the molecule's ionization potential, excitation energies are *only a small fraction of this*. Relative abundances of the singly charged ions change little when electron energies are changed from 30 eV up to 100 eV; the interaction of the bombarding electron and the electrons of the molecule is better viewed as an overlap of force fields, not a sudden collision injecting 50+ eV into the molecule. In fact, substituent effects on the relative abundances of particular ions from certain benzoyl derivatives correlate well with common *ground-state* reactions, such as the ionization of benzoic acid; excited aromatic electronic states would lead to exalted resonance effects for meta substituents (*8.3*).

Ionization of the molecule, which takes place in roughly 10^{-15} second, initially yields the excited molecular ion without change in bond length. According to the quasi-equilibrium theory (*8.4*), all of the energy states of this ion are accessible by radiationless transitions, so that the excitation energy is *internally* redistributed in the ion. A certain fraction of these energy states corresponds to activated complexes which can decompose. The rate of a particular decomposition reaction is determined by the concentration of the activated complex times its rate of crossing the energy barrier. The relative abundances of the ions produced will depend on the rates of the individual decomposition reactions, and thus on the free energies of activation of the corresponding transition states. The abundance of a particular ion depends on the rates of all reactions producing this ion *and* on the rates of all of its decomposition reactions.

$$\text{ABC} \xrightarrow{-e^-} \text{ABC}^{+} \xrightarrow{k_1} \text{A}^+ + \text{BC} \cdot \qquad (8\text{-}1)$$

$$\xrightarrow{k_2} \text{A} \cdot + \text{BC}^+ \qquad (8\text{-}2)$$

$$\xrightarrow{k_2'} \text{B}^+ + \text{C} \qquad (8\text{-}3)$$

$$\xrightarrow{k_3} \text{C} \cdot + \text{AB}^+ \qquad (8\text{-}4)$$

$$\xrightarrow{k_3'} \text{A}^+ + \text{B} \qquad (8\text{-}5)$$

Thus in reactions (8-1)–(8-5) the abundance of BC^+ ions depends on k_2 and k_2', and the abundance of A^+ ions on k_1, k_3, and k_3'. Remember that the ion source pressure is kept so low that usually any bimolecular or other collision reactions will be negligible. The reactions of concern here are only *unimolecular* — an excited ion decomposes to form another ion and one or more neutral species.

The chemistry of such ion decomposition reactions can be viewed as another field of chemistry, but fortunately for most chemists studying this book, there are many close similarities to pyrolytic, photolytic, radiolytic, and other energetic reactions, and there are even many general similarities to condensed phase (solution) organic reactions. The largest points of difference are that ionic and usually radical species are involved in each reaction, and their combined effects sometimes appear unusual to the organic chemist. Most chemists are also unaccustomed to thinking of rearrangement reactions, although these are no longer treated as basically suspicious phenomena. We shall attempt to show in this chapter that there is a strong tendency for these ion decomposition reactions to occur through chemically reasonable processes.

8.1.   Basic Factors Influencing Ion Abundances

The principal fragment ion peaks in the mass spectrum of a particular compound should correspond to *the most stable ion products of the most favorable reaction pathways.* Although this "rule" may appear to be obvious, it serves both as a useful guide for spectral interpretation and as a basis for this chapter's discussion of the mechanisms of unimolecular ion decompositions (*1.11, 3.3, 8.2*).

The most favorable reaction pathways for ion decomposition appear to be determined by a number of driving forces:

(1) Reactions leading to the most stable products, both ionic and neutral, are generally favored. When a heteroatom such as N, S, or O is present, product stability is often achieved by the formation of a "new bond" to the heteroatom (*1.11, 3.3*).

(2) Reactivities within the decomposing ion often parallel reactivities known from chemical reactions in solution. Separate consideration of the reactivities of the radical and ionic sites in the decomposing ion is often useful, as there appear to be different specific reactions characteristic of radical sites and of ionic sites.

(3) Steric factors also parallel those of solution chemistry in some cases, especially for rearrangements to radical sites.

The most stable ion products are abundant because of the influence of the stability of a particular ion on the rate of its formation [driving force (1), above]. Additionally, considering two or more different ions which are possible as products of a *particular* reaction pathway, the most stable of these ions should be the most abundant. Thus both reactions (8-1) and (8-2) involve cleavage of the A-B bond. The more stable of the two possible ion products, A^+ or BC^+, will have its abundance reduced less by subsequent decomposition, such as by reaction (8-3). Similarly, in the decomposition pathway leading to B^+ through reactions (8-2) and (8-3), the relative stabilities of BC^+ and B^+ will be reflected in their observed relative abundances. Structural factors that can stabilize an ionic product include (roughly in order of their importance)

(1) *electron sharing* from a neighboring group, such as in an amine, $\overset{+}{C}H_2-NH_2 \leftrightarrow CH_2=\overset{+}{N}H_2$ (this will be discussed in Section 8.2);

(2) other *resonance effects,* such as in the allyl cation, $\overset{+}{C}H_2-CH=CH_2 \leftrightarrow CH_2=CH-\overset{+}{C}H_2$; and

(3) the *inductive effect,* such as exhibited by the *tert*-butyl

carbonium ion (no attempt will be made to distinguish this effect from that of hyperconjugation). In addition to the influence on ion stabilization, inductive release and withdrawal of electrons, as well as polarizability, can markedly influence bond cleavages.

GENERAL EFFECTS OF STRUCTURE.   The rate of a particular ion decomposition reaction is determined by the activation energy, ΔF^*, necessary to reach the transition state. The structure of the transition state appears to resemble the structure of the products more closely than it resembles the structure of the reacting ion. A structural change that changes the free energy of the products, either the ion or the neutral fragment, usually influences the free energy of the transition state. Thus a molecular modification giving a higher energy product (or products) raises the ΔF^*, and the formation of a more stabilized product (or products) lowers ΔF^*. Structural modifications that change the lability of a bond in the reacting ion will also affect the free energy of activation. Some of these structural effects can be rationalized on the basis of their effect on the probability of stabilizing the unpaired electron and positive charge at particular sites in the ion.

The structural factors of greatest general importance involve the influences of functional groups, and these influences can often be rationalized in mechanistic terms familiar to the organic chemist.

CHAIN BRANCHING.   The mass spectra of alkanes provide a good illustration of the "rule" concerning the preference for the most stable ion products of the most favorable reaction pathways. Ionization must remove a *bonding* electron from a saturated hydrocarbon. Although the resulting positive charge must be delocalized to some extent over the whole molecule, the abundant

$$
\begin{array}{ccc}
& H & H \\
& | & | \\
CH_3\,CH_2 - C - CH_2\,CH_2\,CH_2\,R & \xrightarrow{-e^-} & CH_3\,CH_2 - C \overset{+}{:} CH_2\,CH_2\,CH_2\,R > \\
& | & | \\
& CH_3 & CH_3
\end{array}
$$

$$
\begin{array}{ccc}
H & & H \\
| & & | \\
CH_3\,CH_2 \overset{+}{:} C - CH_2\,CH_2\,CH_2\,R & > & CH_3\,CH_2 - C - CH_2\,CH_2\,CH_2\,R \\
| & & \overset{\bullet+}{} \\
CH_3 & & CH_3 \quad\quad (8\text{-}6)
\end{array}
$$

ion products can be rationalized assuming initial favored removal
of an electron from the most polarizable bond (8-6). Polarizability should be increased by chain branching and by increased
size of the adjacent alkyl groups.

Again following the "rule," the most stable product resulting
from cleavage of the one-electron bond species will be the most
stable carbonium ion (tertiary > secondary > primary) (8-7).

$$
\underset{\underset{CH_3}{|}}{CH_3\,CH_2-\overset{\overset{H}{|}}{C}} \colon CH_2\,CH_2\,CH_2\,R \;\rightarrow\; \underset{\underset{CH_3}{|}}{CH_3\,CH_2-\overset{\overset{H}{|}}{C}{}^{\bullet}} \;>\; {}^{+}CH_2\,CH_2\,CH_2\,R
$$

(8-7)

As discussed in Chapter 4, for larger hydrocarbons such favored
product ions of *primary* reactions may be of much lower abundance than secondary ion products such as $C_3H_7^+$ and $C_4H_9^+$,
so that their relative significance with increasing molecular weight
should be kept in mind.

The spectra of three octane isomers are shown in Unknowns
8.1–8.3, along with the spectrum of n-C_8H_{18}. As we follow the
outline of Table A-1 to elucidate these spectra, information such
as elemental compositions and molecular ion identities is known
from the fact that these are octanes. There are no abundant odd-
electron ions besides $M^{\ddagger}$. The relative molecular ion stabilities
are striking, indicating that Unknown 8.1 is similar to the straight-
chain isomer, while Unknowns 8.2 and 8.3 are highly branched.
The key to the structure lies in the alkyl ion series C_nH_{2n+1}. In
Unknown 8.1 the $(M - CH_3)^+$ ion abundance is dramatically different from that of n-C_8H_{18}, indicating methyl branching. Methyl
substitution on the 3- or 4-position should cause increased
$(M - C_2H_5)^+$ and $(M - C_3H_7^+)$ peaks; the structure of Unknown
8.1 is actually 2-methylheptane. Note the decrease in structural
significance with decreasing mass—the $C_4H_9^+$ abundance is quite
misleading.

Unknown 8.3 also has a very significant $(M - CH_3)^+$ peak, but
the low abundance of M^+ indicates a number of branching methyl
groups. Again the low intensities of $(M - C_2H_5)^+$ and $(M - C_3H_7)^+$ ions eliminate a number of isomeric possibilities. The
true structure, $(CH_3)_3C—C(CH_3)_3$, is supported by the 100%
$C_4H_9^+$ and the low intensity $C_3H_7^+$.

Unknowns 8.1–8.3

	Relative abundance			
m/e	$n\text{-}C_8H_{18}$	8.1	8.2	8.3
15	3.0	4.1	2.3	5.6
26	1.9	1.5	1.3	0.43
26.0 m	0.35	0.22	–	–
27	29.	28.	20.	8.3
28	6.2	4.5	3.2	1.6
29	34.	27.	21.	16.
29.5	0.09	0.07	0.04	0.17
30	0.74	0.60	0.49	0.31
32.8	0.02	0.62	0.09	0.26
38.2	0.04	–	0.21	–
39	13.	15.	9.4	8.5
39.2	0.48	0.57	0.35	0.14
40	2.4	2.8	1.2	1.4
41	38.	38.	24.	27.
42	15.	41.	2.3	1.5
43	100.	100.	100.	17.
44	3.3	3.2	3.4	0.60
45	0.05	0.06	0.05	0.03
53	1.7	1.9	2.6	1.3
54	0.77	0.66	0.59	0.28
55	10.	10.	7.7	4.1
56	18.	7.9	2.5	26.
57	34.	73.	27.	100.
58	1.4	3.1	1.2	4.3
59	0.03	0.04	0.03	0.06
69	1.2	1.2	5.5	1.4
70	12.	17.	0.65	0.12
71	23.	12.	0.46	0.33
72	1.2	0.69	0.03	0.03
73	0.02	0.03	–	–
83	0.11	0.09	0.23	0.77
84	5.9	0.79	16.	0.33
85	29.	1.7	63.	0.03
86.0 m	–	0.24	–	–
86	1.9	0.12	4.1	–
87	0.05	–	0.10	–
98	0.06	3.4	0.15	0.04
99	0.07	12.	1.8	6.1
100	0.01	0.93	0.14	0.47
101	0.01	0.03	0.03	0.03
113	–	0.08	–	–
114	6.7	4.9	0.00	0.02
115	0.55	0.42	–	–
116	0.03	0.01	–	–

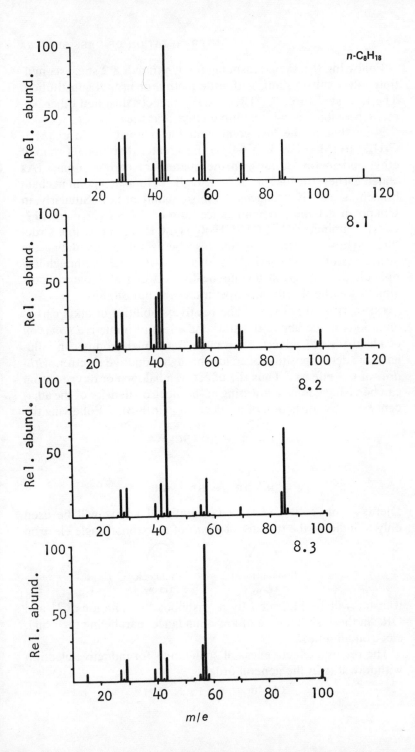

Following the same reasoning for Unknown 8.2 suggests multiple ethyl substitution, with little methyl or propyl substitution. The true structure, $(C_2H_5)_3$—CCH_3, reflects this, and other isomeric possibilities with multiple ethyl branches do not.

Note that in the last compound the intensity ratio of $(M - C_2H_5)^+$ to $(M - CH_3)^+$ is 64/1.9, far greater than the 3/1 ratio of ethyl and methyl groups on the quaternary carbon atom. (As stated earlier, the loss of the *largest* alkyl group at a point in chain branching usually produces the most abundant ion.) Similarly, in Unknown 8.1 the low abundance ratio of $(M - C_2H_5)^+$ to $(M - CH_3)^+$ eliminates $C_2H_5CH(CH_3)(CH_2)_3CH_3$ as a possible structure. These principles should also be useful in elucidating the structures of the isomeric Unknowns 8.4–8.6 (*1.3*), although it is difficult to distinguish unequivocally between all isomeric possibilities without reference spectra. (See pp. 88, 89.)

INDUCTIVE EFFECT.   The relative stabilities of alkyl carbonium ions noted above illustrate the effect of inductive *donation* of electrons (+*I* effect). Particular functional groups can influence the decomposition of an ion through inductive electron-*withdrawal* (−*I* effect). Thus the effect of a halogen or oxygen atom can be visualized as a lowering of the electron density of the adjacent bond by attraction of its electron pair (8-8). (Following the

$$R \overset{\frown}{-} \overset{+\cdot\cdot}{Cl} \rightarrow R^+ + \cdot Cl$$

(8-8)

$$R \overset{\frown}{-} \overset{\cdot\cdot}{O}R' \rightarrow R^+ + \cdot OR$$

Djerassi convention (*1.5*), a conventional arrow will be used only to indicate the transfer of a *pair* of electrons; single electron

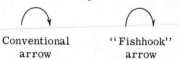

Conventional   "Fishhook"
arrow   arrow

transfer will be indicated by a "fishhook.") The ions Cl^+ and OR^+ in these spectra are of low abundance, paralleling their high electron affinities.

The relative effectiveness of such atoms for inductive electron withdrawal is in the general order

$$Cl > Br, O, S > I \gg N, C, H$$

(Note that the most important four elements exhibiting this effect can usually be distinguished by their natural isotopic abundances.) Despite its high electronegativity, fluorine has been omitted because other cleavages typical of F seem to overshadow its inductive effect, especially cleavages leading to F-containing ions. The lower rate of the reaction $RF^{\ddagger} \rightarrow R^+ + F\cdot$ is due at least in part to the high strength of the C-F bond. The influence of a fluorine atom in a compound on its mass spectrum is similar to that of a nitrile group.

Paralleling experience with organic reactions in solution, the inductive effect drops off rapidly with separation of the functional group from the particular bond through one or more intervening bonds. For polyvalent atoms, especially oxygen and sulfur, the effectiveness also depends on the identity of the other group attached to the heteroatom. The ·OH radical is lost preferentially only if attached to a very labile site, such as in R_3COH, while ·OR loss is much more highly favored. This is due at least in part to the stabilization of the radical by the alkyl group.

For unsaturated heteroatom functional groups such as carbonyl, a similar effect can account for the favored cleavage of the bond connecting this group to another group capable of forming a stable ion. The effect may be visualized as involving another canonical form of the radical ion (8-9).

$$R'-\overset{\overset{+\cdot}{\overset{\displaystyle O}{\|}}}{C}-R \quad \left(\longleftrightarrow R'-\overset{\overset{\displaystyle O\cdot}{|}}{\overset{+}{C}}-R \right) \quad \rightarrow R'-\overset{\overset{\displaystyle O}{\|}}{C}\cdot \; + \; R^+ \qquad (8\text{-}9)$$

POLARIZABILITY.   The influence of polarizability on the site of electron removal was noted in the ionization of alkanes. Similarly, the effect exerted by inductive electron withdrawal on a particular bond also depends on the polarizability of the electrons at that site (8.2). Table 8-1 shows that the inductive effect of a strongly electronegative group, such as chlorine in Cl—C—C,

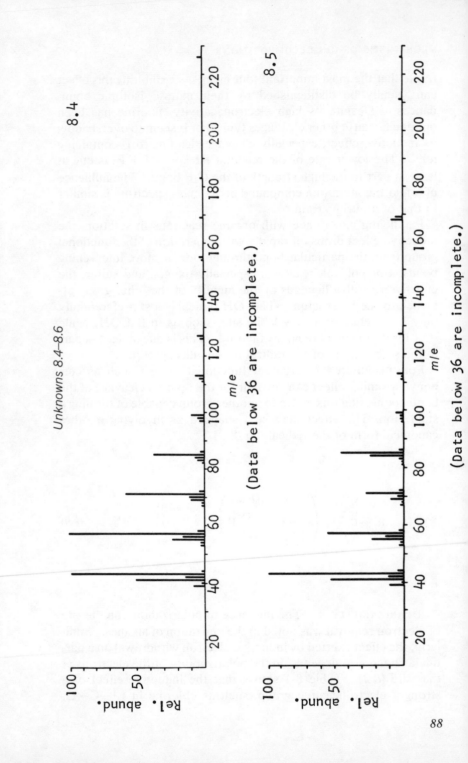

Unknowns 8.4–8.6

8.4

(Data below 36 are incomplete.)

8.5

(Data below 36 are incomplete.)

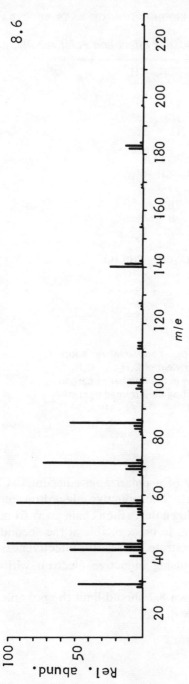

8.6

(Data below 36 are incomplete.)

89

TABLE 8-1.   *Influence of Inductive Effect and Polarizability*

$$X—CH_2—CH_2—CH_3$$

	1	2	3
Cl	55	34	1
Br	65	16	1
I	53	11	1

$$X—CH_2—\overset{\displaystyle CH_3}{\overset{|}{CH}}—CH_3$$

	1	2	3
Cl	6	78	0
Br	41	38	0
I	43	22	0

$$X—CH_2—CH_2—CH(CH_3)_2$$

	1	2	3
Cl	17	17	48
Br	29	14	41
I	25	7	41

The figures represent per cent relative abundances based on total ion yield of $C_nH_{2n-1}^+$, $C_nH_{2n}^+$, and $C_nH_{2n+1}^+$ ions, where n is the number of carbon atoms in the hydrocarbon fragment formed by cleavage of the bond indicated.

can reduce the electron density of a polarizable adjacent C-C bond in addition to the Cl-C bond. The inductive effect drops off rapidly with increased distance down the carbon chain away from the substituent, so that it appears to be negligible at the second C-C bond. The data also demonstrate the relative effectiveness of the different elements in causing inductive electron withdrawal.

The mass spectrum of Unknown 8.7 should limit the possible structures to a few isomers at most.

Unknown 8.7

m/e	Relative abundance	m/e	Relative abundance
15	0.17	70	3.9
27	7.0	71	1.7
28	1.5	72	0.15
29	10.	77	0.99
30	0.22	78	0.09
36	0.43	79	0.31
38	0.27	83	4.2
39	5.4	84	0.83
40	0.78	85	0.22
41	21.	90	0.23
42	3.6	91	0.55
43	21.	92	0.10
44	0.70	93	0.18
45	0.16	98	8.4
53	2.6	99	22.
54	0.92	100	1.6
55	19.	105	0.22
56	6.5	107	0.08
57	100.	112	0.24
58	4.4	119	4.7
59	0.14	120	0.31
63	1.1	121	1.5
64	0.16	122	0.11
65	0.57	148	0.12
69	3.3	150	0.03

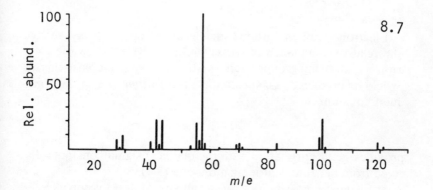

8.7

RESONANCE EFFECTS.   It should not be surprising that resonance stabilization can provide very abundant product ions in a
hydrocarbon spectrum. Both allylic and benzylic bonds are
favored cleavage sites (8-10). Meyerson and his co-workers (4.1)

$$R-CH_2-\overset{\overset{\displaystyle CH_2^{\cdot +}}{\diagup\diagup}}{CH} \quad \rightarrow \quad R\cdot \; + \; CH_2\overset{+}{=\!=}\overset{\overset{\displaystyle CH_2}{\diagup\diagup}}{CH}$$

(8-10)

$$R-CH_2-\overset{+}{\underset{\cdot}{\bigcirc}} \quad \rightarrow \quad R\cdot \; + \; \overset{+}{\bigcirc}$$

have shown that the structure of the ion formed in the latter reaction is not benzyl, but actually the resonance-stabilized tropylium
ion.

Mesomeric (resonance) supply or withdrawal of electrons can
also influence the rate of cleavage of a particular bond of the decomposing ion even when it can cause no change in the product
ion stability.   A number of meta- and para-substituted benzoyl
compounds show this quite dramatically, including acetophe-
nones, benzophenones, benzoic acids, and methyl benzoates
(8.3).

(8-11)

Electron-supplying groups such as amino and hydroxyl reduce
the relative abundance of the acylium ion $RC\!\equiv\!O^+$, while electron-withdrawing groups such as nitro and cyano increase this, as
would be predicted. To substantiate this further, use of the Ham-
mett equation

$$\sigma\rho = \log k/k_0$$

provides good correlation with the classical sigma constants de-
rived from benzoic acid ionization data (8.3).

The isomeric possibilities for the alkylphenols, Unknowns 8.8–
8.10, are narrowed greatly by consideration of their mass spectra
(see pp. 94–97).

SEPARATION OF THE REACTIONS OF RADICAL AND IONIC SITES. It has been proposed recently (*8.5a*) that a more generally satisfactory approach to mass spectral mechanisms involves the *separate* consideration of the effect of the positive ion and radical sites in light of their known behavior in condensed systems. It is important to recognize that the specific reactions possible for each are markedly different and characteristic. Among the most important of these are the following.

Radical site: Formation of an *additional* bond to an adjacent atom through donation of the unpaired electron plus transfer of an electron (indicated by fishhook arrow) from another bond to the adjacent atom; formation of a new bond from the radical site to some other atom by rearrangement (usually abstraction of a hydrogen atom by the radical site with concomitant elimination of a stable molecule).

Cation site: Transfer of an electron pair (indicated by conventional arrow) to move the site of the positive charge, or cleavage of a bond to the charged site by formation of a new bond to a rearranging atom or group (usually with concomitant elimination of a stable neutral species).

For example, the heteroatom of ethers can be viewed as triggering two of the abundant general reactions for these compounds. One reaction can be visualized as involving transfer of an electron to pair with the unpaired electron on the oxygen atom, while the other reaction involves transfer of an electron pair to the positive charge, which is also on the oxygen atom (8-12). The

$$R'\!-\!CH_2\!-\!\overset{+\cdot}{O}\!-\!R \;\rightarrow\; R'\!\cdot \;+\; CH_2\!\!=\!\!\overset{+}{O}\!-\!R$$
$$R'\!-\!CH_2\!-\!\overset{+\cdot}{O}\!-\!R \;\rightarrow\; R'\!-\!CH_2\!-\!O\cdot \;+\; R^+$$

(8-12)

general nonrearrangement reactions of carbonyl compounds can be explained similarly (8-13).

$$R\!-\!\overset{\overset{+\cdot}{O}}{\underset{\|}{C}}\!-\!R' \;\rightarrow\; R\cdot \;+\; {}^+O\!\equiv\!C\!-\!R'$$

$$R\!-\!\overset{\overset{+\cdot}{O}}{\underset{\|}{C}}\!-\!R' \;\rightarrow\; R^+ \;+\; \cdot C\!-\!R'$$

(8-13)

Unknowns 8.8–8.10

m/e	Relative abundance 8.8	8.9	8.10		m/e	Relative abundance 8.8	8.9	8.10
15	0.09		0.06		92	0.30	0.38	0.24
27	0.67	0.88	0.85		93	0.27	0.69	0.13
28	0.28	0.90	0.53		94	0.12	0.12	0.52
29	2.8	2.3	2.2		95	0.51	0.22	3.2
39	1.4	1.0	1.7		103	0.62	1.5	0.35
40	0.15	—	0.20		104	0.20	0.38	0.07
41	5.7	2.8	5.8		105	1.1	1.4	0.49
42	0.22	—	0.23		106	0.21	0.20	0.41
43	0.65	0.59	0.98		107	2.3	3.9	9.2
51	1.2	0.67	0.50		108	0.22	0.33	0.74
52	0.59	0.22	0.16		109	0.15	—	0.16
53	0.86	0.75	0.58		115	2.1	2.0	0.55
54	0.07	—	0.06		116	0.74	0.65	0.16
55	1.3	1.7	1.3		117	1.0	1.2	0.18
56	0.09	—	0.14		118	0.23	0.24	0.14
57	18.	4.7	8.2		119	0.88	0.76	1.6
57.5	0.23	—			120	0.26	0.41	0.56
58	1.1	0.29	0.38		121	0.94	5.9	0.77
59	0.22	—	—		122	0.11	0.60	0.07
60	2.4	—	—		128	1.2	0.8	0.09
60.5	0.22	—	—		129	0.72	1.4	0.06
63	0.50	0.37	0.31		130	0.17	0.94	—
63.5	0.09	—	—		131	0.67	1.0	0.23
64	0.90	0.23	0.16		132	0.28	0.40	0.10
64.5	0.15	—	—		133	1.1	2.9	0.57

134	0.45	0.73	2.2
135	1.7	1.7	100.
136	0.20	0.19	10.
147	1.4	3.00	0.08
148	0.59	5.0	0.04
149	0.86	1.3	0.74
150	0.12	0.13	0.19
161	1.3	1.6	—
162	0.20	1.1	—
163	4.6	3.2	—
164	0.60	0.39	—
165	0.07	—	0.09
175	3.1	1.1	—
176	0.55	—	—
177	0.33	100.	—
178	—	13.	—
190	0.31	—	—
191	100.	—	0.21
192	14.	4.0	0.03
193	1.2	0.59	—
194	0.09	—	—
205	0.15	0.81	—
206	15.	15.	3.8
207	2.6	2.4	0.60
208	0.25	0.21	0.06

65	1.1	0.92	1.2
65.5	0.11	—	0.03
66	1.6	0.21	0.30
66.5	0.19	—	—
67	0.64	0.28	0.16
71	0.09	—	0.07
72	0.78	—	0.03
72.5	0.33	—	—
73	3.6	—	—
73.5	0.86	—	—
74	7.9	—	—
74.5	0.88	—	—
75	0.22	—	0.09
76	0.15	0.14	—
77	1.9	2.2	2.2
78	0.48	0.50	0.42
79	1.0	—	0.67
87	0.15	—	—
87.5	0.90	—	—
88	3.5	—	—
88.5	0.46	—	—
89	0.36	0.26	0.21
90	0.10	—	0.09
91	2.7	3.1	2.2

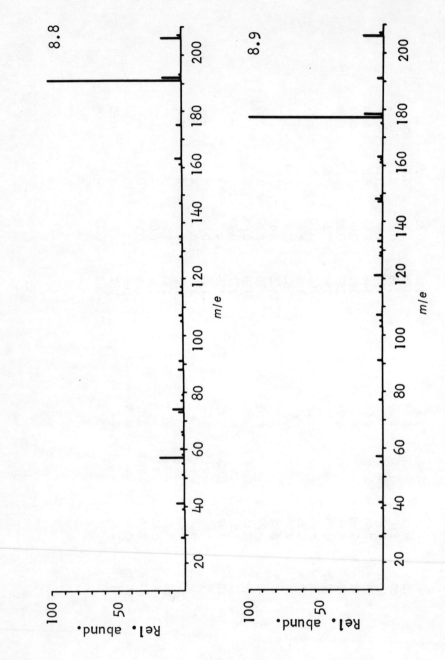

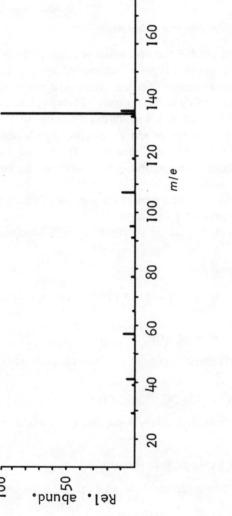

8.10

The separate consideration of the reactivities of the ionic and radical sites is especially valuable when these sites are separated in the ion, or when the ion has no radical site (that is, is an even-electron ion). Many such cases occur in later discussions.

8.2.   Reactions Involving the Cleavage of One Bond

The energy factors discussed in the preceding section will now be applied to some of the general types of unimolecular ion decomposition reactions found in mass spectra. We find it useful to classify these reactions according to the number of bonds cleaved in the process, since this number has a direct relation to the odd- or even-electron nature of the product. Secondary classifications include whether a "new bond" has been formed in the products, and whether the decomposition is accompanied by rearrangement.

An odd-electron ion, such as the molecular ion, may decompose through one of two general pathways:

(1) Loss of an odd-electron radical to yield an even-electron ion:

$$OE^{\ddagger} \rightarrow OE\cdot + EE^{+}$$

(2) Loss of an even-electron molecule to yield an odd-electron ion:

$$OE^{\ddagger} \rightarrow EE + OE^{\ddagger}$$

For the first pathway, only the cleavage of one bond is necessary, for example,

$$CH_3CH_2 \rightarrow CH_2CH_3{}^{\ddagger} \rightarrow CH_3CH_2{}^{+} + \cdot CH_2CH_3$$

To form a radical ion, such as $C_2H_4{}^{\ddagger}$, a second bond must be cleaved, for example,

$$CH_3CH_2 \rightarrow CH_2CH_2 \rightarrow H^{\ddagger} \rightarrow C_2H_4{}^{\ddagger}$$

Cleavage of three bonds can again produce an even-electron ion:

$$CH_3CH_2 \rightarrow CH_2CH \overset{\overset{\displaystyle H^{\ddagger}}{\times}}{\underset{\underset{\displaystyle H}{\times}}{}} \rightarrow C_2H_3{}^{+}$$

Decomposition of an even-electron ion can also proceed through two pathways:

(3) Loss of an even-electron molecule to yield an even-electron ion:

$$EE^+ \rightarrow EE + EE^+$$

(4) Loss of an odd-electron radical to yield an odd-electron ion:

$$EE^+ \rightarrow OE\cdot + OE^+$$

For even-electron ion decompositions the nature of the products is *not* dependent on the number of bonds cleaved; either reaction (3) or (4) can occur when only one bond is cleaved, depending on whether the decomposition is heterolytic or homolytic (8-14).

$$CH_3-CH_2-CH_2-CH_2^+ \rightarrow CH_3-CH_2^+ + CH_2=CH_2$$
$$CH_3-CH_2-CH_2-CH_2^+ \rightarrow CH_3-CH_2\cdot + CH_2^{+\cdot}CH_2 \qquad (8\text{-}14)$$

(As mentioned earlier, the Djerassi convention (*1.5*) of using a conventional arrow to indicate the transfer of a pair of electrons and a fishhook arrow to indicate transfer of a single electron will be followed.)

Not only do these four different types of reactions fulfill the requirement of conservation of charge, but also the requirement that the number of unpaired electrons remains the same, except in reaction (4). In general the latter pathway has a much *lower* probability owing to the formation of two radical sites from an electron pair in the even-electron reactant ion.

CLEAVAGE OF ONE BOND.   If the missing electron of the molecular ion of a hydrocarbon is viewed as being localized in a particular bond, this is then a one-electron bond. Its structure is then already approaching that of the transition state involved in cleaving this bond (8-15).

$$CH_3{:}CH_3 \rightarrow CH_3{:}CH_3^+ \rightarrow CH_3^+CH_3 \rightarrow CH_3\cdot + CH_3^+ \qquad (8\text{-}15)$$

(The symbol $^+$ at the end of the molecule signifies an odd-electron ion without designating the radical site. Use of either $\cdot$ or $^+$ within the molecule, as $CH_3{}^+CH_3$, implies localization of the

radical or the charge.) In such a reaction the single electron of
the cleaved bond may be viewed as remaining with one of the
fragments to produce the neutral radical, so that the other fragment then becomes the even-electron ion product.

Such simple cleavage reactions involving charge localization
in a particular bond are important for hydrocarbons, and for substituted hydrocarbons in which the interaction of the functional
group is primarily through an inductive effect (that is, does not
involve the nonbonding or π electrons). Unless such a reaction
has a strong driving force, such as the formation of a tertiary
carbonium ion, it in general does not lead to abundant fragment
ions. The introduction of a single polar functional group into a
large alkane molecule can dramatically alter its mass spectrum.
Such reactions are taken up in the remainder of the chapter.

NEW BOND FORMATION.   The introduction of a heteroatom
that contains nonbonding outer shell electrons, such as nitrogen,
oxygen, or sulfur, almost always causes very significant changes
in the spectrum. A general way of visualizing these heteroatom
effects is to postulate that the initial positive charge of the molecular ion is localized on the heteroatom (*1.11, 3.3*). Extensive
use of this "localized charge" concept, notably by Djerassi (*1.5,
1.6*) and Shannon (*8.6*), has demonstrated its utility and convenience. The ionization potential data of compounds containing such functional groups indicate that a molecular ion produced
at threshold energies generally has lost such a nonbonding electron. The usual molecular ion produced with 70-V electrons
contains a quasi-equilibrium distribution of electronic energy
states which is much more difficult to characterize exactly, but
this structure with the heteroatom localized charge appears to be
of general importance in determining favored decomposition
pathways. Whatever the exact picture, a handy rule of thumb
is "look for the heteroatom."

By producing an unpaired electron on a heteroatom, ionization
in effect creates a *radical site*. In common with other radical
species, this radical is highly reactive, although it is limited to
participation in intramolecular reactions. In contrast to the
radical site in the bonding orbital (the one-electron bond), the
heteroatom unpaired electron can lead to *new bond formation*, a
powerful driving force for ion decomposition reactions. Thus,

part of the importance of the "localized charge" can also be viewed as a result of the "localized radical site."

Formation of an even-electron carbonium ion lowers by one the number of bonds to the carbon atom. In contrast, the stable even-electron heteroatom ion actually contains an *additional* bond to the heteroatom; the hydronium ion, H_3O^+, is a familiar example from solution chemistry. In the ion the additional bond is made possible by utilization of the nonbonding orbital of the oxygen atom, that is, H_3O^+ is isoelectronic with ammonia, H_3N.

A common reaction of the radical site for molecular and other odd-electron ions is donation of the unpaired electron to form a double bond to the heteroatom (8-16). Note that the other elec-

$$R:CH_2:\ddot{N}H_2 \quad \xrightarrow{-e^-} \quad R:CH_2:\dot{N}H_2 \quad \rightarrow \quad R{\cdot}CH_2::\overset{+}{N}H_2 \qquad (8\text{-}16)$$

tron to form the new bonding pair comes from an adjacent carbon-carbon bond, leading to its cleavage (8-17). Often only one

$$R{\cdot}CH_2::\overset{+}{N}H_2 \quad \rightarrow \quad R{\cdot} \; + \; CH_2::\overset{+}{N}H_2 \qquad (8\text{-}17)$$

of the arrows is shown for simplicity (*1.5*), and bonds are usually used in place of electron pairs (8-18). The product ion will gen-

$$R{-}CH_2{-}\overset{+\cdot}{N}H_2 \quad \rightarrow \quad R{\cdot} \; + \; CH_2{=}\overset{+}{N}H_2 \qquad (8\text{-}18)$$

erally be formulated as shown, although a second canonical form contributes to the actual structure (8-19).

$$CH_2 = \overset{+}{N}H_2 \quad \longleftrightarrow \quad \overset{+}{C}H_2{-}NH_2 \qquad (8\text{-}19)$$

This reaction is the dominant one in the spectra of primary aliphatic amines; m/e 30 is the most abundant ion for $R = H$ to $R = n\text{-}C_{14}H_{29}$ (*8.7*). The substitution of a terminal hydrogen atom in *n*-decane with an amine group causes the profound change in the spectrum shown in Figure 8-1. The series of even-electron ions pinpoint the striking dissimilarity caused by the single amine group. The 30, 44, 58, . . . series $C_nH_{2n+2}N$ represents a much

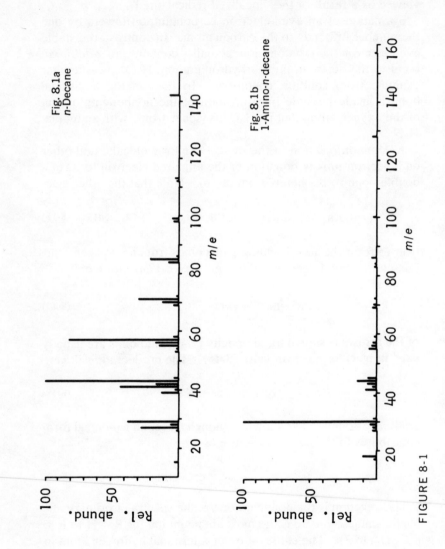

Fig. 8.1a
n-Decane

Fig. 8.1b
1-Amino-n-decane

FIGURE 8-1

102

greater proportion of the total ions than the C_nH_{2n+1} series, illustrating the stabilizing effect of the amino group. Another striking feature in comparing these series is that the most abundant member is now the C_1 ion ($CH_2=\overset{+}{N}H_2$), instead of the C_3 or C_4 ion in the alkyl series. Loss of the largest alkyl group through cleavage of the α-C-C bond is dominant as explained above, but smaller amounts of other $C_nH_{2n}NH_2^+$ ions are also present. Similar "new bond formation" can account for these (8-20).

$$R-CH_2 \quad NH_2 \quad \rightarrow \quad R\cdot \; + \; CH_2-\overset{+}{N}H_2 \qquad (8\text{-}20)$$
$$\underset{(CH_2)_n}{} \qquad\qquad \underset{(CH_2)_n}{}$$

Some further explanation should be given concerning the conventions used by a number of mass spectrometrists, which may appear to contrast with those of the organic chemist. Thus the last reaction could be viewed as an internal displacement of R· by the amine group (8-21). The fishhook of reaction (8-20) may thus

$$\left[H_2\ddot{N} \underset{(CH_2)_n}{\overset{CH_2-R}{|}} \right]^{\ddagger} \rightarrow H_2\overset{+}{N} \underset{(CH_2)_n}{\diagup}^{CH_2} + R\cdot \qquad (8\text{-}21)$$

imply electron flow in the wrong direction. This is a dilemma that has led to a confusing number of conventions in the past. The system used in this book emphasizes for reaction (8-20) that the partial localization of the + charge on N provides a radical site for new bond formation, and the fishhook indicates the electron flow to accomplish this. It should be strongly emphasized, however, that this is merely a system of electron bookkeeping that some have found convenient. The true picture of the ion is a collection of energy states in which the positive charge must be delocalized to some extent over a number of atoms, and thus partial shifts of electrons are involved.

This high tendency for cleavage of the C-C bond to a saturated functional group can provide valuable information concerning the identity of its substituents (8-22). As in the case of chain

$$R_1-\overset{\overset{\displaystyle R_2}{|}}{\underset{\underset{\displaystyle R_3}{|}}{C}}-N\overset{R_4}{\underset{R_5}{\diagdown}} \rightarrow R_1\cdot \; + \; \overset{R_2}{\underset{R_3}{\diagup}}C=\overset{+}{N}\overset{R_4}{\underset{R_5}{\diagdown}} \qquad (8\text{-}22)$$

branching in a hydrocarbon, the most abundant ion formed by
this mechanism is from the loss of the largest alkyl group from
the α-C atom ($R_1 > R_2$ or R_3). In $CH_3CH_2NH_2$ the $(M - 1)^+$
is 20% of the intensity of the $(M - CH_3)^+$; in $CH_3(CH_2)_9NH_2$
(Figure 8-1), the $(M - 1)^+$ is 0.6% of the $(M - C_9H_{19})^+$. If R_4
or R_5 is not hydrogen, cleavage of their C_α-C_β bond will again
give rise to ions with abundances related to the stabilities of the
ions formed, as well as the size of the alkyl groups lost (8-23).

$$R' - CH_2 - \overset{+\cdot}{NH} - CHR - R \rightarrow R' - CH_2 - \overset{+}{NH} = CHR > CH_2 = \overset{+}{NH} - CHR_2$$

$$(8\text{-}23)$$

In using the $C_nH_{2n+2}N$ series (m/e 30, 44, 58, ...) in this
fashion, keep in mind that ions of this formula can also be formed

Unknowns 8.11–8.17

	Relative abundance						
m/e	8.11	8.12	8.13	8.14	8.15	8.16	8.17
15	3.7	3.3	0.71	0.52	3.1	1.3	1.9
27	3.3	11.	2.9	2.7	4.6	10.	0.75
28	4.1	14.	4.6	5.1	9.1	11.	4.2
29	3.6	13.9	2.2	2.2	3.6	8.1	9.1
30	6.2	73.	100.	100.	29.	13.	2.9
31	0.10	1.3	2.1	2.2	1.3	0.27	4.1
32	—	0.38	0.30	0.32	1.8	—	0.39
33	—	—	0.01	—	—	—	1.1
39	4.8	0.81	1.9	0.23	4.2	1.2	2.0
40	1.4	1.3	0.42	0.48	1.1	2.1	0.75
41	18.	3.6	2.9	2.8	7.4	4.5	9.4
42	11.	8.7	1.7	0.42	7.4	28.	6.0
43	2.7	3.2	1.2	5.8	8.8	7.2	3.1
44	0.29	29.	2.0	1.3	1.6	25.	100.
45	—	0.89	0.39	1.6	0.17	1.8	2.8
56	2.7	3.5	1.1	2.1	8.1	7.3	2.3
57	5.6	1.3	0.23	1.1	4.2	5.0	1.6
58	100.	100.	0.30	1.9	100.	100.	10.
59	3.6	3.9	0.02	0.08	3.9	3.9	0.41
71	—	0.36	0.04	0.04	0.58	1.0	0.39
72	—	19.	0.98	1.3	9.6	17.	2.3
73	0.41	31.	10.	10.	11.	23.	1.2
74	0.02	2.0	0.83	0.50	1.3	1.1	0.07

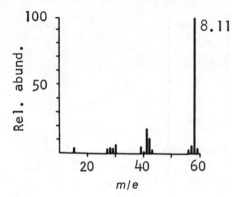

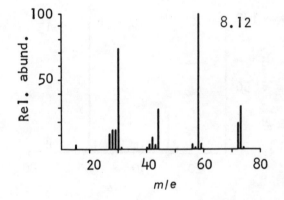

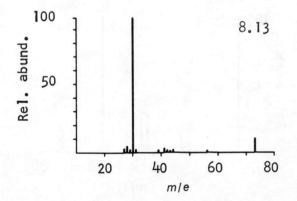

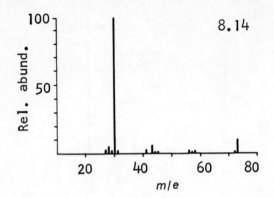

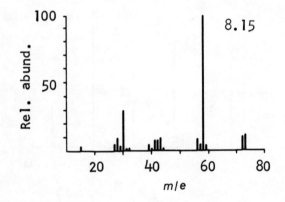

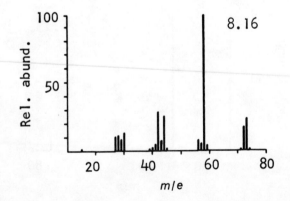

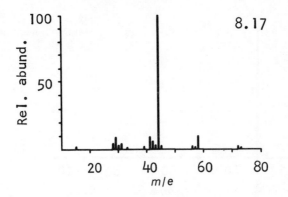

by fragmentation of the bonds further removed from the functional group. Also these ions can decompose further by the loss of olefin or cycloalkane molecules to form secondary ions which also correspond to the formula $C_nH_{2n+2}N$. For example, in Unknown 8.12 m/e 30 is the second largest peak in the spectrum. This is completely incompatible with the base peak at mass 58, $(M - CH_3)^+$, which indicates an α-methyl group. (A C_4 amine cannot contain both a C_1 and a C_3 group on its α-C atom.) Write down all the possible amines of molecular weight 73 containing an α-methyl group. You should have

$$(CH_3)_2\overset{\overset{\displaystyle CH_3}{|}}{C}NH_2,\ C_2H_5\overset{\overset{\displaystyle CH_3}{|}}{C}HNH_2,\ CH_3\overset{\overset{\displaystyle CH_3}{|}}{C}HNHCH_3,\ CH_3CH_2NHC_2H_5,\ \text{and}$$

$$CH_3CH_2N(CH_3)_2$$

The spectrum of Unknown 8.11 should be familiar — you have already encountered it as Unknown 2.9, and it is repeated for comparison. The mechanism for the secondary formation of m/e 30 is discussed later in the chapter; this helps identify Unknown 8.12 as diethylamine.

The other isomeric C_4 amines of Unknowns 8.13–8.17 contain the remaining three α-methylamines; yet in only two is mass 58 the base (largest) peak. Why? This should be obvious from the possible molecular structures.

To assign structures to Unknowns 8.13–8.17, try *predicting* the major ions in the spectra of all the isomeric C_4 alkylamines.

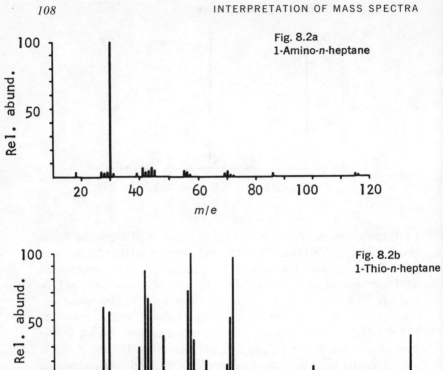

Fig. 8.2a
1-Amino-*n*-heptane

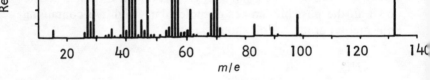

Fig. 8.2b
1-Thio-*n*-heptane

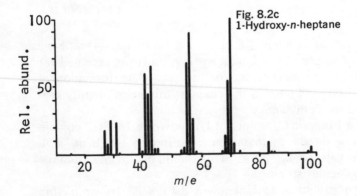

Fig. 8.2c
1-Hydroxy-*n*-heptane

FIGURE 8-2

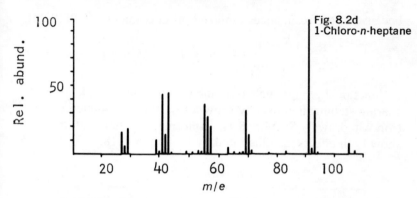

FIGURE 8-2 (*continued*)

The spectrum of one isomer is not included in these unknowns. Which one?

"New bond" formation to a nitrogen atom forms the stable quaternary immonium ion, providing a major driving force for the reaction. This stabilization by electron sharing from the heteroatoms is generally in the order of their strengths as Lewis bases, that is,

$$N > S > O > Cl$$

This can be seen in the spectra of 1-amino-, 1-thio-, 1-hydroxy-, and 1-chloro-*n*-heptane (Figure 8-2). Comparing the abundances of $CH_2{=}\overset{+}{N}H_2$ (*m/e* 30), $CH_2{=}\overset{+}{S}H$ (*m/e* 47), $CH_2{=}\overset{+}{O}H$ (*m/e* 31), and $\overset{+}{C}H_2{-}Cl$ (*m/e* 49) shows a striking gradation. Biemann (*8.8*) has illustrated this effect by competition of the groups in the same molecule. The figures given refer to the abundance of the $XCH_2{}^+$ ion compared to the *total* ion abundance in the spectrum.

$H_2NCH_2{+}CH_2OH$	$HSCH_2{+}CH_2OH$	$ClCH_2{+}CH_2OH$
57% | 2.5%	13.7% | 8.5%	6.4% | 53%

Abundance also depends on relative ion stabilities. Thus in $H_2NCH_2{-}CH(CH_3)NH_2$, the relative abundances (vs. the total ion abundance) of $CH(CH_3){=}\overset{+}{N}H_2$ and $CH_2{=}\overset{+}{N}H_2$ are 46% and 15%, respectively. The ethylene ketal group is even more effective than the amino group in causing cleavage at the C_α-C_β bond because of the resonance-stabilized product ion (*3.6, 8.9*) (8-24).

$$R \underset{R'}{\overset{\overset{+\cdot}{O}-CH_2}{\diagdown C \diagup}} \underset{O-CH_2}{} \rightarrow R\cdot + R'-C \underset{O-CH_2}{\overset{O-CH_2}{\lessgtr}} \quad (8\text{-}24)$$

Functional groups such as amino which exhibit a high electron-sharing stabilization usually show a low effect by inductive electron-withdrawal (Section 8.1). Intermediate heteroatoms can show both effects, as illustrated by Unknown 8.18.

Unknown 8.18

m/e	Relative abundance	m/e	Relative abundance
26	0.38	56	4.8
27	6.1	57	100.
28	1.6	58	4.5
29	15.	59	2.2
29.5	0.35	60	0.09
30	0.55	71	1.7
31	1.2	72	0.23
32	0.05	73	1.1
39	5.6	74	0.05
40	0.97	87	7.9
41	22.	88	0.69
42	2.9	89	0.15
43	9.8	101	0.74
44	1.0	102	0.05
45	3.6	115	0.24
46	0.10	130	2.1
55	2.3	131	0.21

Fluorine shows a surprising tendency for cleavage of the C_α-C_β bond.

$$R—CH_2—F^{\ddagger} \rightarrow CH_2F^+, RCHF^+, \text{ and } R^+$$

When R is C_2H_5, C_3H_7, or C_4H_9, R^+ is abundant. Back-donation of electrons from the fluorine, which can help stabilize the F-containing ions (*8.10*), apparently becomes more important with increased electron demand (CF_3^+ is the most abundant ion from perfluoroalkanes, in sharp contrast to the corresponding hydrocarbons). The high C-F bond strength must reduce the loss of F, and part of the CH_2F^+ may arise from secondary decompositions and rearrangements. However, the $(M - 1)^+$ ions are usually more abundant than the $(M - R)^+$ ions, in sharp contrast to the behavior of amines, ethers, and so on. Apparently retention of the alkyl group is necessary to stabilize the carbonium ion because the contribution of the $CH_2{=}Y^+$ canonical form of Y = F (*8.10*) is less effective than in the case of $Y = NH_2$, OR, and so on. Direct evidence of the strong electron-donating ability of fluorine, despite its high electronegativity, has been shown by Olah (*8.10a*). This is similar to the effect of the strongly electron-withdrawing nitrile group, whose resonance structure $R—CH{=}C{=}\overset{+}{N}$ should be less favorable, with only 6 electrons on N; and to the lowered abundance of the pyridinyl ion in a 2-alkylpyridine (compared to the 3-alkyl derivative), both cases also exhibiting abundant $(M - 1)^+$ ions (8-25).

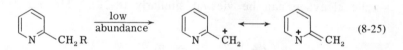 (8-25)

Although electron-sharing stabilization to yield $CH_2{=}X^+$ type ions involving halogens other than fluorine is negligible in general, longer chain *n*-alkyl chloride and bromide mass spectra contain abundant ions which have been attributed to the formation of chloronium and bromonium ions (*8.10*). The spectra of $C_nH_{2n+1}Cl$ (see Figure 8-2) and $C_nH_{2n+1}Br$, where $n = 6$ or above, contain very abundant $C_nH_{2n}Cl^+$ and $C_nH_{2n}Br^+$ ions, particularly with $n = 4$, and to a lesser extent $n = 3$ and 5. For the fragment containing the strongly electronegative halogen atom to retain the positive charge in the cleavage of a particular bond would seem to demand new bond formation (8-26). These ions are not

$$R{-}\overset{+\cdot}{\underset{}{Cl}} \rightarrow R\cdot + \overset{+}{\underset{}{Cl}} \qquad (8\text{-}26)$$

important for fluorides and iodides, and their abundance is greatly lowered by chain branching.

Such cyclic ions also appear to form with other functional groups, but to a much smaller extent (see Figure 8-2). The $C_nH_{2n}Y^+$ ions from thiols (Y = SH) and alcohols (Y = OH) give maximum abundances at $n = 4$, from primary amines (Y = NH$_2$) at $n = 5$, and from nitriles (Y = CN) at $n = 5$ to 7 (possibly due to the 180° bond angle of —C≡Ṅ—) (*8.11*). Such structures are postulated as stable ion intermediates in solution S_N1 internal displacement reactions.

To broaden the "new bond" classification of reactions, it is convenient to portray the effect of hydrocarbon π electrons in a similar fashion to the nonbonding electrons of heteroatoms (8-27).

$$R—CH_2—\overset{+CH_2}{\underset{\cdot}{CH}} \quad \rightarrow \quad R\cdot \; + \; CH_2 \overset{CH_2}{=\overset{+}{CH}} \qquad (8\text{-}27)$$

In this case, however, the new bond to the allylic position is formed at the expense of the original double bond, and the driving force comes from the increased resonance stabilization. Benzylic cleavage can be viewed similarly (8-28). The ionized

$$R—CH_2—\overset{\cdot+}{\bigcirc} \quad \rightarrow \quad R\cdot \; + \; \overset{+}{\bigcirc} \qquad (8\text{-}28)$$

double bonds are purposely shown as polarized to emphasize the localized radical site as an important driving force. Allylic cleavage is enhanced by stabilization of this polarized form, such as by substitution of a methyl group on the carbon bearing the positive charge.

UNSATURATED FUNCTIONAL GROUPS. Functional groups which contain an unsaturated heteroatom can produce abundant ions through a "new bond" mechanism formulated very similarly to that for saturated groups. The carbonyl group is a common example (8-29). (The second pair of nonbonding electrons of the

$$\underset{Y}{\overset{R}{>}}C=\ddot{O} \quad \xrightarrow{\;-e^-\;} \quad \underset{Y}{\overset{R}{>}}C\overset{+\cdot}{=}O \quad \rightarrow \quad R\cdot \; + \; Y—C\equiv\overset{+}{O} \qquad (8\text{-}29)$$

oxygen atom has been omitted for simplicity, and the other conventions used for the saturated functional groups are continued.) In this case the "new bond" formation results in the acylium ion, which is isoelectronic with R—C≡N and whose stability is well known. Again, the product ion can be alternatively viewed as a carbonium ion Y—$\overset{+}{C}$=O in which the charge is stabilized by electron sharing from the adjacent oxygen atom. Such reactions are typical of a wide variety of unsaturated functional groups, such as aldehydes, ketones, esters, carbonates, amides, sulfones, and phosphates. It is interesting that the nitrile group shows little of this α cleavage (8-30). This is as expected, since forming

$$R\overset{\frown}{—}C\equiv\overset{\curvearrowright}{N} \nrightarrow R\cdot + C\equiv\overset{+}{N} \qquad (8\text{-}30)$$

the fourth bond to the nitrogen atom for such a species would cause obviously serious orbital distortion (*8.11*).

Unknown 8.19 is the spectrum of a pure component trapped from a gas chromatographic separation. The only information available beside retention time was a crude infrared spectrum indicating a carbonyl group.

Unknowns 8.20–8.22 are relatively simple molecules. If you have trouble in pinpointing the elemental composition of the m/e 58 peaks, Unknown 2.3 shows the spectrum of one possibility. An instructive approach for such small molecules is to write down all the possible structures that will correspond to this molecular weight, and try to predict their spectra.

EVEN-ELECTRON ION DECOMPOSITION. Favored decomposition processes for even-electron ions generally involve the formation of another even-electron ion and an even-electron molecule, as explained earlier in this chapter. None of the reactions typical of a radical site should now be possible. This process usually involves formation of a new bond to compensate for the one cleaved (8-31). This type of decomposition involves moving of the charge site with *elimination* of a molecule. Such elimination reactions will be enhanced if the charge can be stabilized better at the new site. If such a site is present, how-

Unknown 8.19

m/e	Relative abundance	m/e	Relative abundance
15	6.2	53	13.
26	5.8	54	2.2
27	43.	55	100.
28	7.4	56	5.7
29	46.	57	0.51
30	1.1	58	0.84
31	1.0	59	0.22
36.8 m	0.87	67	1.5
37	3.2	68	0.32
38	7.2	69	0.30
39	42.	70.3 m	1.5
40	5.2	82	1.3
41	13.	83	97.
42	6.8	84	5.4
43	90.	85	0.33
44	2.2	97	0.04
45	0.41	98	51.
51.1 m	0.29	99	3.5
52	2.4	100	0.20

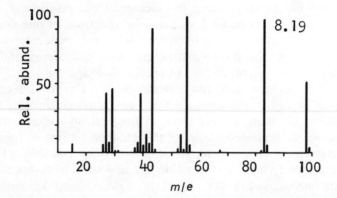

Unknowns 8.20–8.22

m/e	Relative abundance 8.20	8.21	8.22
14	2.1	4.7	2.0
15	4.4	6.0	14.
26	10.	21.	3.1
27	34.	45.	4.8
28	62.	25.	4.7
29	100.	80.	3.0
30	6.4	24.	0.15
31	3.5	60.	0.51
37	3.3	6.8	1.7
38	3.5	9.4	1.9
39	7.3	39.	4.2
40	1.2	11.	0.83
41	2.8	7.6	1.9
42	3.2	2.1	6.7
43	3.9	6.0	100.
44	2.2	0.20	2.4
45	0.91	0.39	0.39
55	2.3	6.2	0.35
56	0.98	8.1	0.03
57	18.	100.	1.1
58	64.	26.	37.
59	2.4	1.1	1.2
60	0.16	0.08	0.09

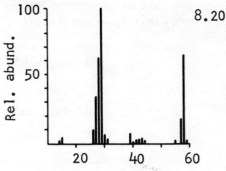

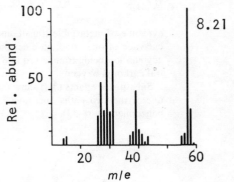

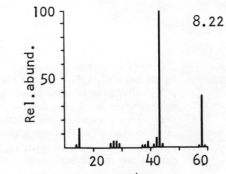

ever, the same ion may well be produced with facility in a primary decomposition process.

$$R \overset{\frown}{-} CH_2 \overset{\frown}{-} CH_2^+ \rightarrow R^+ + CH_2 = CH_2$$

(8-31)

$$R \overset{\frown}{-} \underset{|}{CH_2} \overset{\searrow}{\underset{|}{CH_2^+}} \rightarrow R^+ + \underset{|}{\overset{CH_2 - CH_2}{\underset{CH_2 - CH_2}{|}}} \\ \quad CH_2 - CH_2$$

For heteroatom-containing even-electron ions, a "new bond" may already have been formed in producing the ion. Djerassi and his co-workers (*8.12*) have found the reaction (8-32) to occur, from

$$R \overset{+\cdot}{-} \overset{\frown}{O} \overset{\frown}{-} CHR' \overset{\frown}{-} R'' \xrightarrow{-R''} R \overset{\frown}{-} \overset{+}{O} = CHR' \rightarrow R^+ + O = CHR' \quad (8\text{-}32)$$

evidence of metastable transitions. Here there is an apparent net cleavage of one bond, an electron pair in a bonding orbital of the acylium ion being transferred into a nonbonding orbital of the neutral carbonyl oxygen.

Substituent effects (*8.3*) show that a similar reaction is involved in one of the two paths operative in producing the phenyl ion from benzophenone (8-33).

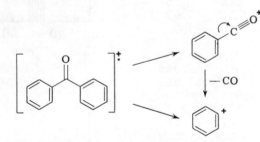

(8-33)

A word of warning is necessary here. An abundant ion formed by the loss of C_2H_4 from a higher even-electron ion does not necessarily indicate the presence of $-CH_2-CH_2^+$ in the latter ion. Rearrangements, as discussed below, are common in hydrocarbon moieties, so that ion formation by such a C_2H_4 loss is only indicative of some type of alkyl grouping in the larger ion. However, the principles involved do eliminate or make less probable certain decomposition mechanisms, such as (8-34). The probability of the first reaction is low because of the high energy of the neutral fragment. The second reaction involves the formation of two odd-elec-

$$R-CH_2-CH_2^+ \quad \not\longrightarrow \quad R-CH_2^+ \; + \; CH_2:$$
$$\not\longrightarrow \quad R-CH_2-CH^{+\bullet} \; + \; H\bullet$$

(8-34)

tron species. Thus the alkyl ions, $C_nH_{2n+1}{}^+$, in normal paraffins are not formed by sequential loss of methylene groups. Also in a spectrum containing an abundant $C_5H_{11}{}^+$ ion, an abundant $C_5H_{10}{}^{+\ddagger}$ ion should be mainly formed from some other ion of higher mass. The rearrangement decomposition of even-electron ions is discussed in Section 8.5.

8.3. Multiple Cleavages: Cyclic Molecules

If two bonds are cleaved in the decomposition of an odd-electron ion, the products (if there are only two products) must now be an *odd-electron ion* and an even-electron molecule, in contrast to the products of the cleavage of one bond. Two general cases involve such multiple cleavage—cyclic molecules and rearrangement reactions. Cyclic molecules will be discussed in this section.

Cleavage of a single ring bond in a cyclic molecule yields an ion of identical mass (and elemental composition). Therefore cleavage of a second bond is necessary to produce a discernible fragment ion. If this is viewed as a stepwise process (although many reactions may well be concerted), the initial odd-electron ion product will contain both a charge and a radical site. The second step involves loss of an even-electron molecule by an elimination in which either the ion or the radical site may be shifted (8-35). (Alternative rationalizations of electron transfers

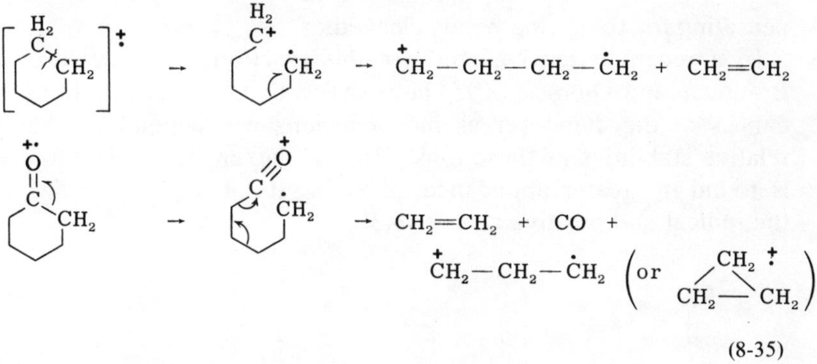

(8-35)

are obviously possible for either reaction.) It should be mentioned again that the decompositions involving aliphatic moieties are higher energy processes, and are generally overshadowed by pathways due to unsaturation or heteroatom functional groups present in an ion. Any analogous process (8.13) (8-36) is much

$$
\overset{+\cdot}{H N} C_2 H_5 \quad\longrightarrow\quad \overset{+\cdot}{H N} C_2 H_5 \; + \; 2\,CH_2 \!=\! CH_2 \tag{8-36}
$$

less abundant for *N*-ethylcyclohexylamine than a rearrangement yielding a new bond to the nitrogen atom.

UNSATURATED CYCLIC MOLECULES — THE RETRO DIELS–ALDER REACTION.   The presence of a double bond in the ring makes possible a pathway which is analogous to the retro Diels–Alder reaction (8.14). This often can lead to a sizable peak in the spectrum in the absence of other structural features undergoing particularly facile cleavages. Two alternative ion products are possible (8-37). Two new bonds are formed in the products com-

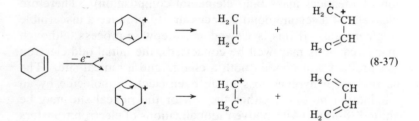

$$\tag{8-37}$$

pensating for the 2 ring bonds cleaved.

In a recent extensive study of this reaction, Budzikiewicz, Brauman, and Djerassi (8.15) have shown that the relative abundances of the diene versus monoene ions will depend on the relative stabilities of these ions. In cyclohexene the $C_4H_6^+$ ion is found in greater abundance, reflecting its ability to stabilize the radical and positive charge (8-38).

$$\tag{8-38}$$

The pronounced differences between the spectra of *trans*-Δ^2-octahydronaphthalene (R = H) and its 9-methyl derivative (R = CH$_3$) (*8.15*) can be rationalized similarly (8-39). The relative

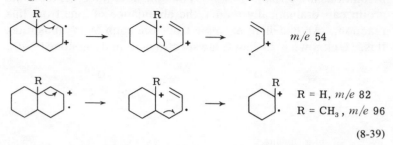

$$R = H, m/e \ 82$$
$$R = CH_3, m/e \ 96$$

$$m/e \ 54$$

(8-39)

abundances in Figure 8-3 show the influence of the inductive charge stabilization of the added methyl group.

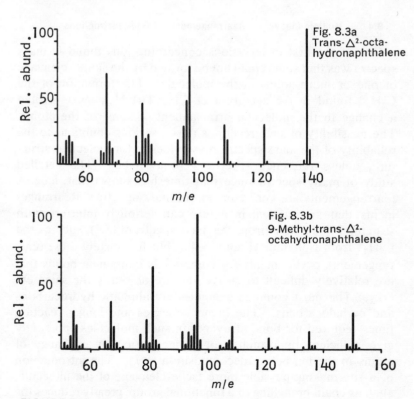

Fig. 8.3a
Trans-Δ^2-octa-hydronaphthalene

Fig. 8.3b
9-Methyl-trans-Δ^2-octahydronaphthalene

FIGURE 8-3

As with other hydrocarbon fragmentation reactions, the retro Diels–Alder reaction will be important only if no preferable fragmentations are possible (*8.15*). Thus the addition of a functional group can dramatically reduce the abundance of ions from this reaction. An excellent example from Biemann (*8.14*) illustrates this. Unknown 8.23 shows the spectra of α- and β-ionone (8-40).

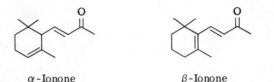

(8-40)

α-Ionone   β-Ionone

Pair the structures and spectra, and justify your choice.

8.4.   Multiple Cleavages: Rearrangements of Odd-Electron Ions

One of the first observations concerning ions found in mass spectra was that some could not be formed by the simple cleavage of one or more bonds in the molecule. The formation of the $C_2H_5^+$ found in the spectrum of $CH_3CH(CH_3)_2$ must involve a change in the molecular arrangement of some of the atoms. The possibility of such reactions raised serious doubts as to the reliability of the mass spectrum as evidence for molecular structure, unless reference spectra were available. The detailed study of many spectra since that time has shown that, indeed, rearrangements are very common in mass spectra. Rearrangements that are *random* in nature can seriously interfere with structural deductions from the mass spectrum (*8.1*), such as the $C_2H_5^+$ from isobutane (Figure 8-4a), but fortunately these rearrangements occur mainly for compounds containing bonds that are relatively difficult to cleave and are of nearly the same energy. The most common examples are aliphatic hydrocarbons and perhalocarbons. The higher energies and longer reaction times required for bond cleavages in such molecules apparently give sufficient opportunity for isomerization or exchange of atoms in the ion before decomposition (*8.1*). The introduction of a site making possible more facile cleavage of the molecule, such as chain branching or a functional group, greatly reduces the importance of such randomizing pathways. For example, the

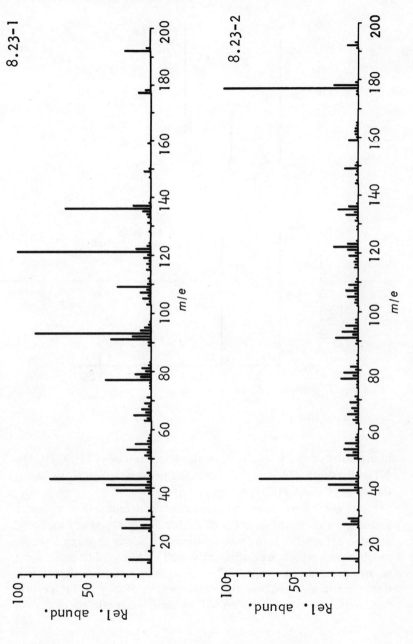

8.23-1

8.23-2

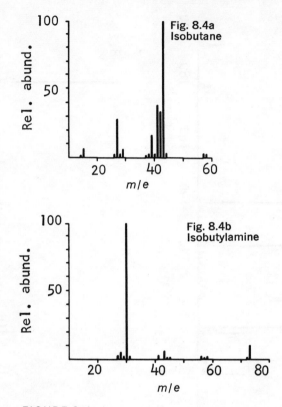

FIGURE 8-4

abundance of the $C_2H_5^+$ ion in the spectrum of $(CH_3)_2CHCH_2$-NH_2 (Figure 8-4b) is greatly reduced in comparison to its abundance in $(CH_3)_2CHCH_3$.

However, there are rearrangement processes that produce abundant ions in the spectra of molecules containing functional groups. Happily, many such processes occur through *specific* mechanisms which are sufficiently well understood to make such rearrangement ions valuable for molecular structure determination. Examples include the requirement of a γ-H for certain reactions, and the "ortho effect" in some aromatic spectra. As with the reactions discussed previously, most of the important rearrangement mechanisms involve decomposition of molecular and other odd-electron ions, and these will be discussed first, starting with those which yield odd-electron product ions.

To the chemist used to dealing with the reactions of organic compounds in solution, the types of rearrangements encountered in mass spectrometry may seem strange, and therefore suspect. There are many parallels with other kinds of *unimolecular* reactions of organic compounds, however, such as the vapor phase dehydration of alcohols, formation of olefins by the pyrolysis of acetates through loss of acetic acid, and the "Norrish type 2" photolytic rearrangement loss of olefins from ketones, as well as parallels in radiation chemistry. There are usually only a limited number of reactions by which the initially formed molecular ion can decompose through a simple bond cleavage that has a low energy requirement. Rearrangements can provide alternate pathways in which the reacting center attacks another part of the ion. This might be considered as a "bimolecular" reaction in which the reacting species are in the *same ion* instead of a second molecule (*3.3*). Obviously, steric factors can be of major importance in such reactions, paralleling the importance of steric effects on intramolecular rearrangements in ordinary chemical reactions. For many functional groups, the "new bond rule" is a useful concept for explaining these reactions and identifying them in an unknown spectrum. The new bond formed to the functional group provides a pathway to the stable products, although the functional group may not have gained a net whole bond in the final product.

SPECIFIC HYDROGEN REARRANGEMENTS. Rearrangement of a hydrogen atom to a polar functional group of an odd-electron ion leads to major peaks in the spectra of many classes of compounds.* The second largest peak in the spectrum of 4-methyl-2-pentanone (Figure 8-5) arises through such a rearrangement (8-41). Compare this with the spectrum of 3-methyl-2-pentanone

---

* Flatteringly referred to by some authors as the "McLafferty rearrangement" (*8.16*).

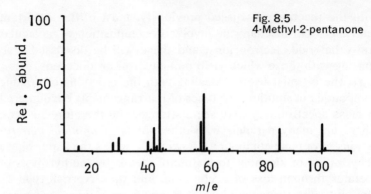

FIGURE 8-5

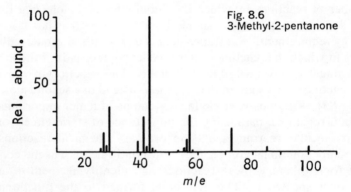

FIGURE 8-6

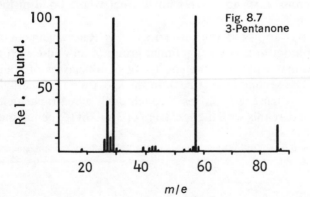

FIGURE 8-7

(Figure 8-6) and 3-pentanone (Figure 8-7), especially noting the odd-electron ions. Thus new-bond formation utilizing the radical site may also be accomplished through rearrangement. Note the similarity of the transition state to that of the retro Diels–Alder reaction shown in the previous section.

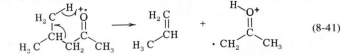

(8-41)

This rearrangement can account for important odd-electron ions in the spectra of aldehydes, ketones, esters, acids, amides, carbonates, epoxides, phosphates, sulfites, ketimines, oximes, hydrazones, nitriles, phenylalkanes, and olefins (*1.5, 2.6, 3.3, 4.1, 8.1*) (8-42).

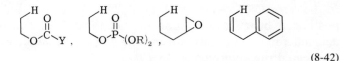

(8-42)

The olefinic product competes with the heteroatom moiety for the positive charge (*3.3*). In the mass spectra of ethyl esters the C_2H_4 peak is unimportant, but in β-phenylethyl esters the corresponding styrene ion (*m/e* 104) is the base (most abundant) peak. Formation of these products may also involve transfer of a hydrogen to the ether oxygen atom (8-43).

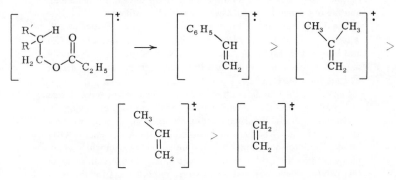

(8-43)

Increased lability of the hydrogen atom increases its tendency to rearrange. Djerassi and his co-workers have greatly clarified our knowledge of rearrangement processes in a recent series of publications. By specific deuterium labeling they have demonstrated that transfer of a secondary H is favored over transfer of a primary H by a factor of *10* (*8.18*) for this ketone (8-44). They

$$(8-44)$$

also have pointed out the favored transfer of an allylic hydrogen in the retro Diels–Alder reaction (*8.15*). Meyerson and Leitch postulated benzylic activation of the transferring hydrogen to account for an unusual rearrangement reaction involving a six-membered ring intermediate (*8.19*).

For a number of compounds [such as esters (*8.20*) and ketones (*8.18*)] the hydrogen atom is transferred almost exclusively from the γ position, in keeping with the mechanism shown. Competing hydrogen transfer through other intermediates beside the six-membered ring intermediate can occur (*8.1, 8.17, 8.21*) because of activation of other hydrogen positions, different steric requirements of the molecular system of the functional group (nitrile, for instance), and factors which have not been completely clarified.

The detailed picture of this mechanism has not been settled (*8.22*), with both migration of hydrogen in the form of a radical (*1.5, 1.6*) and a proton (*8.23*) being suggested. [Both of these are obviously more useful representations than the early formulation indicating a hydride ion transfer (*8.24*).]

Separating the reactivity effects of the radical and positive charge (*8.5a*) appears to offer an explanation consistent with the major observations. Initial hydrogen atom abstraction, $a \rightarrow b$, involves cleavage of a C-H bond with formation of the lower energy O-H bond. Bond formation involves the unpaired electron which occupies a nonbonding orbital on the oxygen atom. The directionality of this orbital should demand strict steric requirements for the rear-

ranging hydrogen atom in order to form the new sp^2 bond in intermediate ion *b* (8-45). Electron transfer to the new radical site in *b*

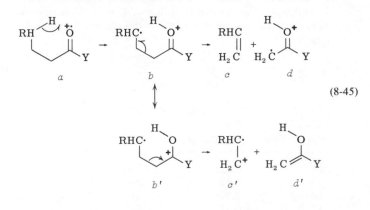

(8-45)

now yields the final product ion *d*. Formation of the alternative
olefin ion can be viewed as resulting from transfer of an electron
pair to the canonical form of the intermediate ion, *b'*. Electron-
donating groups, such as R = alkyl or phenyl, will aid electron pair
transfer. In some cases the ion *c'* is prominent even when the
stabilizing group in R is too far removed for interaction through
the chain (*8.23*). This may indicate an interaction through space, or
it is possible that the hydrogen abstraction triggering the rearrangement has been caused by an $n \rightarrow \pi^*$ excitation of the carbonyl.
The prevalence of this rearrangement reaction ("Norrish type 2")
in photochemistry makes such an additional path plausible.

In general, the rearrangement provides a low energy pathway for
the formation of a stable molecule and a new ionic species in
which the radical site can be delocalized. Several resonance forms
of the radical ion *d* can be drawn, such as (8-46). The ion is

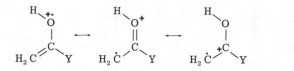

(8-46)

actually isoelectronic with the allyl radical and should enjoy a
similar resonance stabilization.

The prominent odd-electron ions of Unknowns 8.24 and 8.25 should provide clues to their molecular structures.

The common nonrearrangement cleavage of unsaturated heteroatom functional groups occurs at the α-C-C bond, while this rearrangement reaction causes cleavage at the adjacent β bond (8-47).

(8-47)

Unknown 8.24

m/e	Relative abundance	m/e	Relative abundance
14	0.21	55	1.4
15	0.97	56	1.7
16	0.39	57	11.
17	0.32	58	1.1
18	2.2	59	100.
27	6.4	60	2.9
28	2.1	61	0.25
29	9.8	69	3.7
30	0.83	70	0.21
31	0.69	72	0.54
32	0.11	73	3.4
39	7.1	74	0.05
40	1.0	85	1.7
41	17.	86	11.
42	6.4	87	0.54
43	20.	88	0.03
44	31.	100	1.3
45	1.3	101	1.7
46	0.90	102	0.10

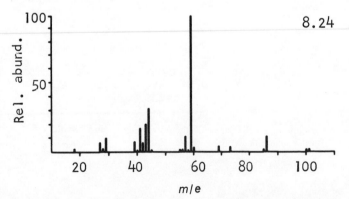

Unknown 8.25

m/e	Relative abundance	m/e	Relative abundance
15	0.34	63.5	0.05
26	1.2	64	1.0
27	11.	65	10.
28	1.1	66	0.74
29	3.9	67	0.07
30	0.09	76	0.62
38	1.2	77	5.9
39	10.	78	6.2
39.1 m	0.17	79	2.7
40	0.91	80	0.24
41	5.3	88.0 m	0.18
42	0.40	89	1.7
43	2.7	90.0 m	1.7
44	0.15	91	100.
44.5	0.02	92	55.
46.4 m	0.21	93	3.8
50	2.7	94	0.14
51	7.4	103	2.0
51.5	0.07	104	1.4
52	1.9	105	8.5
53	1.1	106	1.0
54	0.14	115	1.0
55	0.50	116	0.31
56	0.51	117	0.68
56.5	0.02	118	0.12
57	0.17	119	0.85
57.5	0.63	120	0.08
58	0.27	133	0.09
58.5	0.08	134	24.
59.4 m	0.05	135	2.6
63	3.3	136	0.13

8.25

For olefins, the *same* bond is cleaved in both reactions (*8.30*), a consequence of the parallel drawn earlier between the nonrearrangement allylic or benzylic cleavage and that cleavage common to saturated heteroatom functional groups. This anomaly can be explained (*8.5a*) on the basis of different polarizations of the C=C double bond for the reactions (8-48a,b). For a surprising number of methyl-substituted olefins, reaction (8-48a) produces the base peak

$$H_3C \quad +CHR \qquad \rightarrow \quad C_2H_5{}^{\cdot} \;+\; \qquad CHR$$

(8-48a)

(8-48b)

when $R = CH_3$, $R' = H$, and reaction (8-48b) produces the base peak when $R = H$, $R' = CH_3$ (*8.30*). This is in accord with inductive stabilization of the positive charge at the particular site by the methyl group. The relative abundances of the corresponding rearrangement ion, m/e 106, in the mass spectra of *m*-tolyl- and *p*-tolyl-1-propane are 5.5% and 0.9%, respectively, compared to the abundances of the ion from benzylic cleavage, m/e 105 (8-49, 8-50).

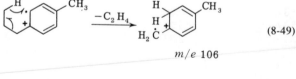

(8-49)

m/e 106

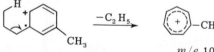

(8-50)

m/e 105

Consecutive rearrangements can also occur, with aliphatic ketones exhibiting a classic example (*8.28*) (8-51). (This re-

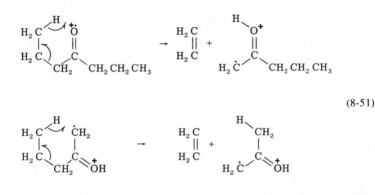

(8-51)

action is also called a "double hydrogen rearrangement" (*8.1*), but in this book the latter name will be reserved for rearrangements of two hydrogen atoms in a single reaction.)   A recent publication from Djerassi's laboratory (*8.18*) shows that the second hydrogen atom in such ketones also originates almost entirely from the γ position.

The consecutive rearrangement is reduced appreciably in the case of the corresponding esters (8-52), probably because of the stability of the intermediate ion (*8.5a*).

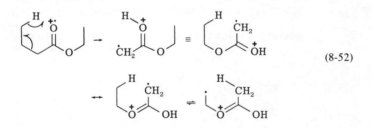

(8-52)

Rearrangements of larger groups, such as methyl, have been observed, but it is difficult to predict these with our present understanding (*8.1, 8.31, 8.32, 8.33*).

REARRANGEMENTS IN SATURATED MOLECULES.   If there is no double bond in the molecule, rearrangements are also possible which can be visualized as involving "new bond formation."   A common example, loss of H_2O from alcohols, may be pictured as

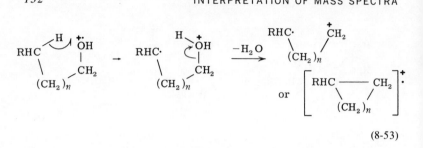

$$(8\text{-}53)$$

(8-53). The similar loss of H_2S is observed in thiols, and of HF and HCl in alkyl fluorides and chlorides. Although the position of origination of the rearranged H is less specific than for many of the unsaturated functional groups, there is a pronounced preference for the 6-membered ring transition state for alcohols (*8.34*) and the 5-membered ring transition state for bromides and chlorides (*8.34b*) paralleling the tendency found for formation of the cyclic "onium" ions.

The addition of a structural feature more capable of stabilizing a positive charge on the heteroatom *lowers* the probability of this reaction. Loss of NH_3 from primary amines is uncommon because of the basicity of N. Loss of HOR from ROR is much less abundant than loss of HOH from ROH due to the inductive stabilization by the alkyl group. The favored loss of CH_3COOH from acetates reflects the electron-attracting power of the acetyl group. Similarly, loss of HCl is favored over loss of HBr.

Spiteller (*8.23*) and Djerassi (*1.5*) have pointed out that a similar rearrangement mechanism can also explain other abundant ions

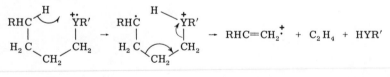

$$(8\text{-}54)$$

from compounds containing saturated heteroatom functional groups (8-54). R' can be a group such as

$$\overset{O}{\overset{\|}{-CR''}} \quad \text{in the ester} \quad R(CH_2)_4O\overset{O}{\overset{\|}{C}}R''$$

as well as H or alkyl.

In some saturated compounds the group containing the heteroatom apparently can retain the positive charge after such a rearrangement. The base peak in the spectrum of dicyclohexyl ether
(8-55) corresponds to the ion which would be formed by the loss of

$$\text{(structure)} \rightarrow C_6H_{12}O^{+\cdot} + C_6H_{10} \qquad (8\text{-}55)$$

cyclohexene. The mechanism may well be quite different, as olefin
loss is uncommon for acyclic ethers. For example, the mechanism
could involve initial oxonium ion formation through ring opening,
followed by elimination of the other ring with hydrogen rearrangement to the oxygen, or possibly with hydrogen abstraction by the
new radical site.

The "ortho effect" can be pictured as arising through such a
reaction in which the rearranging hydrogen atom is activated by
the aromatic ring. Although ortho, meta, and para aromatic
isomers generally show only small differences in their spectra,
this rearrangement can serve to identify the ortho isomer for a
variety of structures (*8.25, 8.26, 8.27, 8.28*) (8-56). The spatial

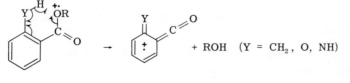

$$+ ROH \quad (Y = CH_2, O, NH)$$

$$(8\text{-}56)$$

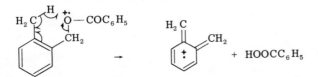

$$+ HOOCC_6H_5$$

arrangement of the unsaturated six-membered ring transition state
is reminiscent of the specific rearrangement of hydrogen to unsaturated functional groups discussed earlier in this section.

The elimination of a *saturated* molecule from any ion (except from some saturated ions formed by rearrangement) involves the rearrangement of a group to the neutral moiety. Elimination of a molecule of ethylene from a cyclohexane ion can be accomplished by the movement of only electrons, but the loss of a molecule of ethane from cyclohexane (or any other molecule) must be accomplished by the rearrangement of one or more atoms to the ejected neutral species, for example, $H\!-\!R\!-\!C_2H_5{}^+ \rightarrow R^{\ddagger} + C_2H_6$. Small molecules that are eliminated easily are mainly limited to those containing an electronegative atom, such as HCl, H_2O, and H_2S (described above); abundant ions are generally not produced by the loss of H_2, CH_4, and C_2H_6 from odd-electron ions. The mechanism given above for the loss of H_2O, HCl, and similar heteroatom-containing molecules would predict this, as there is no site for formation of a new bond on an alkyl group. Surprisingly, in the cleavage at a chain-branching site in an alkane, an extra hydrogen atom may be lost from the ion in addition to the expected loss of the alkyl branch. Thus the abundant odd-electron $C_{10}H_{20}{}^+$ ion in the spectrum of 7-*n*-propyltridecane (Unknown 8.6) can be pictured as arising through the loss of a hexane molecule (8-57). Possibly charge localization

$$H\!-\!(C_6H_{12})\!\diagdown\!\underset{\underset{\displaystyle H_2}{\overset{\displaystyle +\cdot}{\underset{|}{\overset{|}{C}}}\diagdown C_5H_{11}}{\overset{\displaystyle H}{\overset{|}{C}}\diagup C_3H_7} \quad \longrightarrow \quad (C_6H_{12})\!=\!CH\!-\!C_3H_7\!\cdot^+ \;+\; H_3C\!-\!C_5H_{11}$$

(8-57)

at the substituted carbon atom in the molecular ion provides a radical site for rearrangement of the hydrogen atom.

Other rearrangements involving the elimination of a small, stable molecule from an odd-electron ion have been reported (*1.5, 1.6, 1.11, 3.3*). A classic example is the elimination of carbon monoxide, a reaction that has been examined in some detail by Beynon and co-workers (*8.35*) (8-58). The large peaks in the

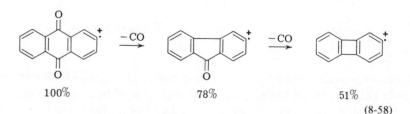

            100%   78%   51%

(8-58)

spectrum of anthraquinone correspond in mass to the molecular ions of fluorenone and diphenylene, formed by the elimination of one molecule and two molecules, respectively, of carbon monoxide.

In benzophenone the corresponding ions $C_6H_5COC_6H_5^+$ and $C_{12}H_{10}^+$ are present in relative abundances of 54% and 2% of the benzoyl ion (the most abundant ion in the spectrum) respectively, reflecting the less favorable entropy of the transition state. The rearrangement loss of CO in the spectra of alkyl phenyl ketones, C_6H_5COR, is negligible. Loss of CO from the molecular ions of diphenyl ether and of phenol yields the corresponding product ions in 25% and 19% relative abundances, respectively (8.35). Although these losses require unusual rearrangement mechanisms, other possible decomposition paths for these stable molecular ions have high energy requirements.

Other neutral molecules whose elimination is commonly observed, such as C_2H_2, $CH_2{=}C{=}O$, CH_2O, CO_2, and HCN are summarized in Table A-5. Try out the principles discussed in this section on Unknown 8.26.

REARRANGEMENTS OF ODD-ELECTRON IONS TO YIELD EVEN-ELECTRON IONS.   Decomposition of an odd-electron ion by cleavage of one single bond yields an even-electron ion, but such a product ion can also be formed by the cleavage of *three* bonds. If one remembers that formation of an odd-electron ion product by the cleavage of two bonds usually arises through decomposition of a cyclic molecule or by the rearrangement of a linear molecule, it is not surprising that the formation of an even-electron ion product through the cleavage of three bonds can arise through the *rearrangement* of a *cyclic* molecule, or through a *double* rearrangement. The concomitant neutral product must be a radical species.

As discussed earlier, cleavage of a ring bond in a cyclic molecular ion can provide both a radical site and a site of localized positive charge. Hydrogen atom abstraction by the radical site, followed by elimination of an alkyl radical, can thus yield the even-electron ion. Such a mechanism can account for the base (largest) peak in both cyclopentanone and N-ethylcyclopentylamine (1.5) (8-59).

Unknown 8.26

m/e	Relative abundance	m/e	Relative abundance	m/e	Relative abundance	m/e	Relative abundance
15	9.2	46	3.6	67	4.9	88	0.74
26	1.3	47	29.	68	18.	89	11.
27	24.	48	1.6	69	59.	90	1.1
29	32.	53	4.7	70	70.	91	0.64
30	0.86	54	5.7	71	15.	98	4.3
33	0.49	55	74.	72	0.83	99	0.36
34	1.1	56	100.	73	0.98	103	0.93
39	19.	57	38.	74	0.64	112	23.
40	4.0	58	2.9	75	1.1	113	2.2
41	76.	59	3.0	82	11.	114	0.12
42	47.	60	4.9	83	46.	145	1.7
43	74.	61	18.	84	51.	146	37.
44	3.3	62	1.6	85	4.9	147	3.9
45	8.2	65	1.4	86	0.28	148	1.8
		66	1.2				

8.26

136

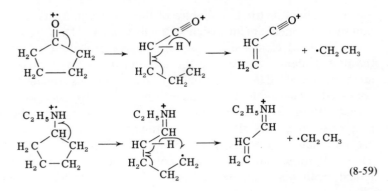

$$(8-59)$$

In the spectrum of des-N-methyl-α-obscurine, a similar mechanism can explain the loss of the —CH_2—$CH(CH_3)$—CH_2— bridge plus a hydrogen atom to form the $(M - 57)^+$ ion (*8.37*) (8-60).

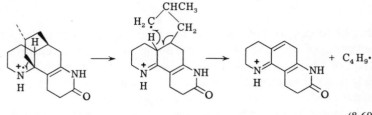

$$(8-60)$$

The $(M - C_4H_8)^+$ is of much lower abundance than the $(M - C_4H_9)^+$.

THE DOUBLE HYDROGEN REARRANGEMENT. When an unsaturated functional group which contains two or more heteroatoms is present, the odd-electron ion can decompose with rearrangement of *two* hydrogen atoms, forming an ion that is often more abundant than that from the "McLafferty rearrangement" of a single hydrogen atom. Esters typically form this rearranged ion,

$$H_2—(C_nH_{2n-1})—O\overset{\overset{\displaystyle O}{\|}}{C}R^{\ddagger} \rightarrow C_nH_{2n-1}{\cdot} + (HO)_2CR^+$$

but it is also a useful indicator for amides, imides, carbonates, and phosphates. This rearrangement leads to the ion $(M - 27)^+$ for $n = 2$, $(M - 41)^+$ for $n = 3$, and so forth (see Table A-5). Such an ion is usually a distinctive feature of the spectrum, as its formation by other mechanisms, such as the loss of a C_nH_{2n-1} group by a vinylic bond cleavage, is generally of low probability. Since the first evidence concerning the mechanism of this rearrangement was reported (*8.36*), a number of papers on this subject have appeared. The evidence has been summarized by Djerassi in a recent definitive study (*8.38*). Deuterium labeling of *n*-butyl propionate indicates that the *two* transferring hydrogen atoms originate mainly from the γ- and δ-atom positions (relative to the carbonyl group, that is, $C_β$ and $C_γ$ of the alkoxy group). A simplified mechanism can account generally for this (8-61). Strong

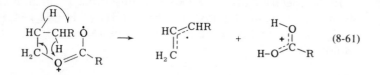

$$(8\text{-}61)$$

driving forces are provided by the symmetry and resonance stabilization of both the radical and ion products. The rearrangement of a hydrogen atom to a charged site is discussed in Section 8.5; this rearrangement can also be visualized as resulting from initial ionization at the saturated oxygen atom.

A double hydrogen rearrangement of aromatic compounds (see Unknowns 7.2 and 7.4) can be viewed as having similar driving forces (8-62).

$$\underline{n}\text{- or } \underline{iso}\text{-}C_3H_7 \text{—} \langle +\cdot \rangle \;\rightarrow\; C_3H_5\cdot \;+\; \langle + \rangle \qquad (8\text{-}62)$$

In Unknown 8.27, what even-electron ion seems unusual? Does this give an indication of the structure?

8.5.   Multiple Cleavages: Decompositions of Even-Electron Ions

Our discussion of the decomposition of even-electron ions has been mainly limited to a few paragraphs at the end of Section 8.2 on nonrearrangement processes. Surprisingly few studies have been reported on these, considering that even-electron ions are

Unknown 8.27

m/e	Relative abundance	m/e	Relative abundance	m/e	Relative abundance	m/e	Relative abundance
15	0.21	51	1.1	79	5.1	124	5.3
27	3.6	52	0.77	80	0.34	125	0.45
28	2.5	55	2.7	104	0.67	134	0.21
29	5.1	56	19.	105	100.	135	1.3
39	2.4	57	1.5	106	8.3	136	0.44
40	0.33	63	0.19	107	1.2	149	0.34
41	6.0	65	0.40	120	0.20	161	0.52
42	0.34	76	2.0	121	0.28	163	0.34
43	0.87	77	37.	122	17.	178	2.0
50	3.0	78	3.0	123	68.	179	0.26

8.27

usually the more abundant ions in the mass spectra of complex molecules, especially ion species of lower molecular weight. This scarcity of studies is largely due to the fact that even-electron ion decompositions must be secondary reactions, and therefore are more difficult to elucidate unambiguously. Both the ion structure and identification of the reaction pathway (that is, which is the intermediate ion) are common problems. The reader should be cautioned that a number of the mechanisms presented in this section have not been proved or tested rigorously. They are presented because the author finds them useful to correlate a sizable body of data that has not been previously treated in a general fashion.

As discussed earlier, the decomposition of an even-electron ion to form an odd-electron ion and a neutral radical should be much less probable than decomposition to form the more stable even-electron ion and molecule. If the latter reaction involves the rupture of one bond, this must be a *heterolytic* cleavage, and thus the site of the positive charge must move (8-63). If the decom-

$$R{:}CH_2{:}CH_2^+ \rightarrow R^+ + CH_2{::}CH_2$$

$$(8\text{-}63)$$

$$R{:}\ddot{O}{::}CH_2 \rightarrow R^+ + {:}\ddot{O}{::}CH_2$$

posing even-electron ion is of importance in the spectrum, its positive charge is probably stabilized. Thus a decomposition pathway involving the shift of the ionic site should be less favorable (8-64). In this example if R^+ is a highly stable ion, it is of

$$R{-}CH_2{-}C(CH_3)_2^+ \not\rightarrow R^+ + CH_2{=}C(CH_3)_2 \qquad (8\text{-}64)$$

little importance analytically whether R^+ is formed by initial cleavage of the molecular ion or by such a secondary decomposition.

Alternatively, decomposition of an even-electron ion to yield a new even-electron ion can be accomplished by *homolytic* cleavage of two bonds (the same requirement as the formation of an odd-electron ion from the decomposition of an odd-electron ion). This situation can arise in the decomposition of a cyclic ion

$$CH_2\!\!=\!\!CH^+ + CH_2\!\!=\!\!CH_2$$

(8-65)

$$R\!-\!C_7H_7^{+\cdot} \xrightarrow{-R^\cdot} C_7H_7^+ \xrightarrow{-C_2H_2} C_5H_5^+ \xrightarrow{-C_2H_2} C_3H_3^+$$

$$\rightarrow HO\!\!\overset{+}{=}\!\!CH_2 + CH_2\!\!=\!\!CH_2$$ (8-66)

(8-65) or by rearrangement (8-66). These reactions will be discussed in later paragraphs of this section.

The main driving force for further decomposition of an even-
electron ion appears to be the formation of two smaller even-
electron products. The neutral species appear to have much the
same stability and electronegativity requirements as those species
formed in the decompositions of odd-electron ions. Common
neutral products include the small molecules HCl, H_2O, CO_2,
C_2H_4, and C_2H_2. For others the reader is again referred to
Table A-5.

DECOMPOSITION OF CYCLIC EVEN-ELECTRON IONS. Few clear
examples of the decomposition of a cyclic even-electron ion are
available because of the possible ambiguities in assignment of reaction pathways. Djerassi and co-workers have pointed out (8.39)
that α-substitution in piperidines greatly affects the mass spectrum.
For 2,6-dimethylpiperidine the most abundant ion is due to α-cleav-
age with the loss of a methyl radical (8-67). The further decomposition of this ion by a mechanism analogous to the retro Diels–Alder
reaction can account for the substantial m/e 70 peak. The latter

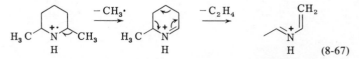

(8-67)

step is isoelectronic with the true retro Diels–Alder reaction, but
does not involve a radical site as does the analog discussed in Section 8.3. Illustrating the ambiguity in elucidating the pathways to
such secondary ions, the m/e 70 peak may also arise through an odd-
electron ion intermediate (8-68).

Decompositions of saturated even-electron cyclic ions must also
occur, such as the cyclobutyl ion used as an example earlier in this
section (8-65).

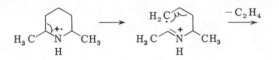

(8-68)

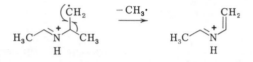

REARRANGEMENT DECOMPOSITION OF EVEN-ELECTRON IONS.
For purposes of structure determination, it can be quite important to recognize the further decomposition of an even-electron
product ion through a rearrangement process. For example,
the mass spectra of 1-hexanol and ethyl butyl ether both show
prominent peaks at m/e 31, ostensibly $(—CH_2OH)^+$. Instead
of being misleading, this rearrangement ion in the ether spectrum
actually is indicative of its structure.

There appear to be a number of general types of rearrangement
reactions which involve elimination of a stable molecule from an
even-electron ion. These reactions cannot involve a radical site,
and it is not entirely clear what role is played by the positive
charge. The rearrangement formation of m/e 31 in ethyl butyl
ether illustrates a main type of such reactions. This reaction is
the classic hydrogen rearrangement involved in the decomposition of even-electron ions formed from amines, ethers, and similar compounds (Y = NR, O, S) (*3.6*) (8-69).

$$H—C_nH_{2n}—\overset{+\cdot}{Y}—CRR'—R'' \rightarrow H\overbrace{\underset{(C_nH_{2n})}{}}\overset{+}{Y}=CRR' \rightarrow C_nH_{2n} + H\overset{+}{Y}=CRR'$$

(8-69)

This can be pictured (*8.5a*) as a displacement of the C_nH_{2n} from
the charged site by the rearranging hydrogen atom, but it is also possible that the hydrogen first rearranges to an excited orbital at the
heteroatom Y (*8.39a*). Whatever the mechanism, this reaction is
usually favored at the site of the charge in such an even-electron ion.

An alternative pathway is possible, but does not appear to be important (8-70). The m/e 31 ion from diethyl ether appears to be of

$$H-C_2H_4-\overset{+\cdot}{O}-CH_2-CH_3 \xrightarrow{\;-C_2H_4\;} \cancel{}\; HO\overset{+\cdot}{-}CH_2-CH_3 \xrightarrow{\;-CH_3\cdot\;} \cancel{}\; H\overset{+}{O}=CH_2$$

$$(8\text{-}70)$$

quite different energy and (or) structure than the m/e 31 ion from ethanol (*8.40*).

Recent definitive papers by Djerassi and Fenselau (*8.12, 8.41*) show, in contrast to the original mechanism proposed (*3.6*), that the probability of rearrangement is roughly equivalent for hydrogen atoms in the β, γ, and δ positions, with a smaller (ca. 10%) contribution from the α position (8-71). These results are consistent with

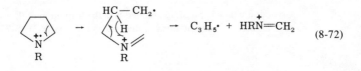

$$(8\text{-}71)$$

the lack of a radical site. The rearrangement cannot involve a hydrogen abstraction, and the nonbonding orbital of the neutral nitrogen atom is no longer available in the immonium ion form for new bond formation in keeping with the lack of specificity of the rearranging hydrogen atom.

It is possible that this rearrangement can proceed even when a radical in site is present in the molecule (*8.42*) (8-72). Such a ra-

$$\underset{\substack{N\\R}}{\langle\!\!\!\langle\, \overset{+\cdot}{}\,\rangle} \;\longrightarrow\; \underset{\substack{N\\R}}{\langle\!\!\!\langle\, \overset{HC-CH_2\cdot}{\underset{+}{}}\,\rangle} \;\longrightarrow\; C_3H_5\cdot + HR\overset{+}{N}=CH_2 \qquad (8\text{-}72)$$

tionale was used earlier in the mechanisms of ester rearrangements (8-61, Section 8.4).

A variety of such elimination rearrangements can be found (8-73). (The last reaction is of much less importance in the spectra of aliphatic esters than in amides.)

$$H(C_nH_{2n})OCO(C_3H_5)H_2 \xrightarrow{-C_3H_5\cdot} H \underset{(C_nH_{2n})}{\overset{+}{\diagdown}} \overset{+}{O}{=}C(OH)_2 \rightarrow C_nH_{2n} + H\overset{+}{O}{=}C(OH)_2$$

$$CH_3\overset{O}{\overset{\|}{C}}{-}\overset{+\cdot}{N}R{-}CH_2{-}R' \xrightarrow{-R'\cdot} H\underset{H_2C-C=O}{\overset{+}{N}R{=}CH_2} \rightarrow CH_2{=}C{=}O + HR\overset{+}{N}{=}CH_2$$

$$(8\text{-}73)$$

The tendency to undergo this rearrangement appears to be N > O > S, although particular cases can be found where oxygen is as effective as nitrogen. Study of this is complicated by other reactions, such as those discussed in the remainder of this chapter.

Displacement at a *carbon* atom adjacent to the functional group Y is also observed for Y = F, SR, phenyl, OR, and NHR (8-74).

$$H(C_nH_{2n}){-}\overset{R}{\underset{}{\overset{|}{C}H}}{-}\overset{+\cdot}{Y} \rightarrow H\underset{(C_nH_{2n})}{\diagup}\overset{+}{CH{=}Y} \longleftrightarrow H\underset{(C_nH_{2n})}{\diagup}\overset{+}{CH{-}Y} \rightarrow \begin{matrix} C_nH_{2n} \\ + \\ CH_2{=}\overset{+}{Y} \end{matrix}$$

$$(8\text{-}74)$$

The probability of this displacement rearrangement is generally (F?) > S, phenyl > O > N, opposite to that noted above for displacement at the charged heteroatom. This may indicate that the carbonium ion canonical form is an important contributor to the intermediate.

A reaction which is possibly analogous is the formation of fluoromethyl carbonium ions at unsaturated carbon atoms (*8.1*) (8-75).

$$CHF{=}CFBr \xrightarrow{-e^-} \cdot\overset{H}{\underset{F\ \ F}{\overset{\diagup}{C}{-}\overset{+}{C}{-}Br}} \rightarrow \cdot\underset{F}{C}: + CHBrF^+ \quad (8\text{-}75)$$

The surprising displacement of the unstable CF species apparently is made possible by the formation of the CHBrF⁺ ion. The unusual stability of such fluoromethyl cations was discussed earlier. Rearrangement of halogen is also possible; the CClF₂⁺ ion is abundant in the spectrum of CClF=CF₂.

Another common decomposition pathway of the even-electron ion involves elimination of the heteroatom Y with a hydrogen atom, presumably by rearrangement loss of HY. (The similar loss of HY from odd-electron ions is discussed in Section 8.4.) The reaction can be visualized as attack of H on the neutral Y to displace a substituent on Y. An intermediate of the reaction could involve hydrogen bonding of H to Y (8-76). No careful

$$H-(C_nH_{2n-1})-Y^+ \rightarrow HY + (C_nH_{2n-1})^+ \qquad (8\text{-}76)$$

study of these rather ambiguous secondary processes has been made. However, again the abundance of the product ion appears to be roughly in the order Y = halogens, CN > SH, OH, SZ, OZ > NH_2, CH_3, H. The abundance is usually reduced when Z is an electron-donating group such as alkyl, but the abundance is favored if Z is an electron-attracting group such as acyl (for example, the loss of CH_3COOH from acetoxy compounds).

Loss of NH_3 usually requires special activation, such as the substitution of alkyl or aryl groups on the β-carbon atom. The losses of H_2 and CH_4 are not usually important reactions in determining structure, but the possibility of this occurrence needs to be recognized to avoid the possibility that peaks from such reactions might be assigned to other, more structurally significant, sources.

When Y = SH, SR, OH, OR, or NH_2, this reaction can compete with the elimination reaction producing the heteroatom-containing ion (8-77).

$$H-C_nH_{2n}-CH\!\!=\!\!\overset{+}{Y} \leftrightarrow \begin{array}{c} Y\searrow \\ H \quad \overset{+}{C}H \\ \diagdown (C_nH_{2n}) \diagup \end{array} \begin{array}{l} \nearrow C_nH_{2n} + CH_2\!\!=\!\!\overset{+}{Y} \\ \\ \searrow (C_{n+1}H_{2n+1})^+ + HY \end{array}$$

$$(8\text{-}77)$$

A molecular ion containing two electronegative substituents commonly undergoes this elimination of HY (8-78).

$$(HC_nH_{2n-1}Y)\overset{\frown}{\underset{+\cdot}{-}}Y' \xrightarrow{-Y'} (HC_nH_{2n-1}Y)^+ \rightarrow HY + (C_nH_{2n-1})^+$$

$$(8\text{-}78)$$

The site of the ionic charge apparently has no large effect on the rate of elimination of HY; the relative abundance of the $(M - HY_2)^+$ ion in dihalo-*n*-butanes appears to be affected little by position of substitution. Part of the driving force for HY loss from the even-electron ion is probably the further resonance stabilization achieved for the positive charge through allylic and similar structures in the product ion. A variety of other reactions (8-79) can be placed in this general classification. The structures

$$CH_3SCH_2CH_2CH\overset{+}{=}NH_2 \rightarrow CH_2\overset{+}{=}CHCH\overset{+}{=}NH_2 \gg \overset{HC=CH}{CH_3\overset{+}{S}-CH_2}$$

$$CH_3\overset{+}{O}\overset{O}{=}CH-\overset{\|}{C}OCH_3 \rightarrow CH_3OH + CH_3\overset{+}{O}=C=C=O \qquad (8\text{-}79)$$

$$\overset{+}{O}\equiv C-\overset{O}{\underset{\|}{C}}-NH_2 \rightarrow H_2O + \overset{+}{O}\equiv C-C\equiv N$$

$$H_2-(C_nH_{2n-1})-C\equiv\overset{+}{O} \rightarrow H_2O + (C_{n+1}H_{2n-1})^+$$

shown are postulates only.

Note that the rearrangement loss of such HY molecules from an *odd-electron* ion is often overshadowed by the simple loss of Y; $(M - HY)^{+\cdot} < (M - Y)^+$. Formation of $(M - HYY')^+$ [from either $(M - Y)^+ - HY'$ or $(M - HY)^{+\cdot} - Y'^{\cdot}$] is much more probable than the formation of either $(M - YY')^{+\cdot}$ (except for compounds highly deficient in H) or $(M - H_2YY')^{+\cdot}$ (except when the location of Y is isolated from that of Y' in the molecule). The specificity of the H lost in the formation of $(M - HYY')$ might indicate the relative importance of the radical site.

The spectra of Unknowns 8.28 and 8.29 illustrate some of the reactions of this section.

Unknown 8.28

m/e	Relative abundance	m/e	Relative abundance
14	1.6	52	3.5
15	4.8	53	0.73
16	0.21	54	76.
17	0.17	55	14.
18	0.75	56	1.3
19	1.2	57	13.
27	23.	58	1.0
28	18.	59	57.
29	39.	60	2.1
30	1.6	61	0.16
31	100.	68	1.7
32	1.5	69	0.39
33	0.23	70	3.0
39	1.2	71	1.0
40	2.5	72	2.0
41	13.	73	0.10
42	5.9	84	9.5
43	6.1	85	0.50
44	1.5	98	3.5
45	13.	99	0.53
46	0.32	100	0.04

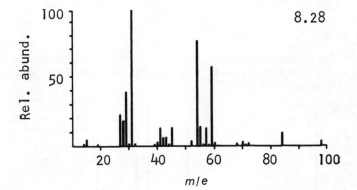

Unknown 8.29

m/e	Relative abundance	m/e	Relative abundance
15	0.72	69	100.
17	0.25	70	8.4
18	1.1	71	3.7
19	0.99	72	7.1
27	20.	73	61.
28	2.0	74	3.0
29	12.	75	0.20
30	0.60	83	1.6
31	11.	84	0.86
32	0.13	85	1.7
39	6.4	86	5.6
40	1.0	87	57.
41	34.	88	3.4
42	4.0	89	0.20
43	33.	96.7 m	0.05
44	9.2	97	0.25
45	11.	99	0.20
46	0.26	111	0.08
55	86.	112 [a]	7.4
56	6.6	113	0.98
57	14.	127	0.29
58	3.6	128	0.50
59	1.0	129 [a]	0.94
67	1.0	130	0.09
68	0.56		

[a] The elemental compositions of the m/e 112 and 129 ions are C_8H_{16} and $C_8H_{17}O$, respectively, by high resolution mass spectrometry.

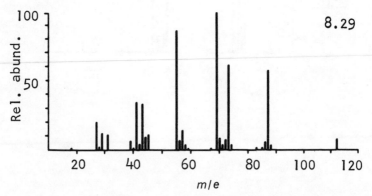

Each of the incomplete spectra of Unknowns 8.30, 8.31, and 8.32 is due to one of these compounds:

$$CH_2{=}C(CH_3)\overset{\displaystyle O}{\overset{\|}{C}}OCH_3 \qquad CH_3CH_2CH_2CH_2CH_2\overset{\displaystyle O}{\overset{\|}{C}}H \qquad CH_3\overset{\displaystyle O}{\overset{\|}{C}}C(CH_3)_3$$

$$CH_3CH_2CH_2CH_2OCH{=}CH_2 \qquad CH_3\overset{\displaystyle O}{\overset{\|}{C}}OCH_2CH{=}CH_2$$

(All of these have a molecular weight of 100.)   Assign the proper structure to each spectrum.

Unknowns 8.30–8.32

	Relative abundance		
m/e	8.30	8.31	8.32
29	32.	4.0	3.4
41	51.	100.	11.
42	3.7	5.3	2.7
43	37.	2.1	100.
44	0.96	3.6	2.6
55	4.3	6.3	0.76
56	7.0	2.7	0.18
57	100.	1.0	7.9
58	4.9	0.85	11.
59	2.3	9.2	0.44
60	0.33	0.37	0.21
61	0.19	0.17	2.7
69	0.87	83.	0.06
70	0.39	4.2	0.02
71	0.27	0.57	0.37
85	4.9	4.7	0.33
99	0.37	10.	0.02
100	26.	51.	0.25

9

MOLECULAR STRUCTURE
POSTULATIONS

All of the information and postulations gathered above must now be utilized to deduce the most logical structure. It is difficult to outline a generally applicable pathway from these to such a deduction, for each case is usually dependent on the particular spectrum and the other available information. Though practice and experience are invaluable in finding the most logical and efficient pathways, some particulars may be helpful.

Molecular structure determination by most spectroscopic techniques involves the basic method of postulating a particular structure, predicting its spectrum, and then comparing this with the unknown spectrum. A main reason for the first seven steps of Table A-1 is that these will generally suggest structures for examination. Thus at this point you should review the information and postulations from these steps and the possible molecular structures which they suggest. Before each of these structures is examined critically, a real effort should be made to list *all* that appear possible, although there is usually sufficient information in the mass spectrum to narrow the structural possibilities rapidly.

The elimination of all but one possibility for the molecular structure of course does not prove that this one is correct, unless a reference spectrum of the compound can be obtained.

9.1. Known Structural Class: Shift Technique

Often other information eliminates many possible structures from consideration. As mentioned in Chapter 1, check all other spectroscopic, chemical, and physical evidence that is available. When such information indicates a particular type of structure, check the mass spectra (*1.5, 1.6, 1.16, 1.17*) and ion decomposition mechanisms (Chapter 8) to be expected. When stable complex molecules are indicated, the "shift technique" can be quite useful (*9.1*). An additional functional group added to such a molecule can change the spectrum by merely increasing the mass of the particular ion fragments which contain this functional group, but without changing the relative abundances of these ions to a great extent. Of course, this will not be true if the group added strongly affects the stability of a particular bond or bonds in the molecular ion. An obvious case is isotopic substitution; deuterium labeling of a compound increases the mass of each ion by one for each D incorporated, but isotope effects on ion relative abundances are generally small (*9.2*). Substitution of a hydrogen by a group of low influence (such as methyl, methoxyl, or chlorine) at an unreactive position (for example, a ring, especially an aromatic ring) often gives ion abundances similar to those of the original spectrum. This technique has been especially useful for the indole alkaloids. These stable ring structures contain functional groups that strongly influence the decomposition, minimizing the effect on the spectrum of molecular substitution. Unknown 9.1 from the work of Biemann and his group (*9.1*) compares the spectrum of an unknown indole alkaloid to two knowns. What functional groups does the unknown contain? Where are they most probably located on the molecular skeleton?

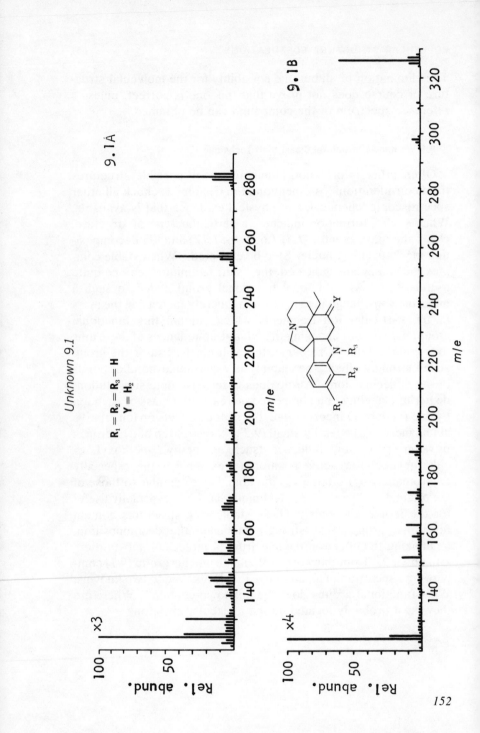

Unknown 9.1

$R_1 = R_2 = R_3 = H$
$Y = H_2$

9.1Á

9.1B

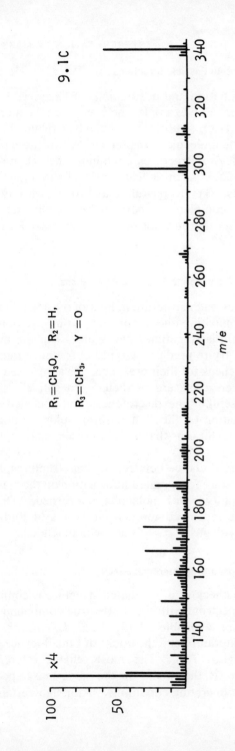

153

9.2. Listing of All Possible Structures

Use the information and postulations of Chapters 1–8 to prepare such a list. For example, the presence of major $C_2H_3O^+$ (*m/e* 43) and $C_2H_5O_2^+$ (*m/e* 61) ions can be explained by an acetate moiety in the molecule (Chapter 7). Seeing these peaks, you should try to devise structures containing the acetate grouping which are consistent with at least some of the other important spectral features. Try to postulate as broad a variety of structures (partial or complete) as possible before eliminating any of them. Record all that are not obviously impossible from other information.

9.3. Critical Evaluation of Structure Postulations

Carefully study each structure in light of the collected information. When eliminating one, record why you have done this, as later reevaluation is sometimes necessary. For the most probable structures, try to predict the types of fragment ions that will be formed, and check for their presence. Be sure to see that there are no ions where none are predicted — "negative" information can be very useful. The discreteness and specificity of mass spectral information (a "line" spectrum) yields as much significance from abundant ions that are *not* present as from those that are present.

In making a final choice between similar structures, be sure to consult the literature for detailed information on the mass spectra of the particular types of molecules concerned. The original literature or the recent comprehensive books of Budzikiewicz, Djerassi, and Williams (*1.5, 1.6*) are recommended.

9.4. Comparison with Reference Spectra

The ultimate check of a postulated structure is comparison of the unknown spectrum with that of the true compound. Several compilations are available (*1.15, 1.16, 1.17, 1.18*), as well as the original literature and the books of Budzikiewicz, Djerassi, and Williams (*1.5, 1.6*). The most reliable reference spectrum, of course, is that made on the same mass spectrometer under the same operating conditions. Although certain isomers give quite similar spectra, spectra that are *identical* with respect to both mass and relative abundance data will almost always demand identical molecular structures, except in the case of optical isomers.

9.5. Examples

The best way to become proficient in interpreting mass spectra is practice. The following unknowns have been designed to illustrate the above principles in a variety of combination. The discussion above was mainly an outline of the techniques involved, and a number of the fine points are discussed in the answers to the unknowns. For more details, the reader is referred to the literature.

Unknown 9.2

m/e	Relative abundance	m/e	Relative abundance
12	1.5	38	2.0
13	2.9	39	2.8
14	7.3	40	5.8
15	20.	41	5.1
16	0.60	42	18.
17	0.30	43	14.
27	8.0	44	100.
28	68.	45	51.
29	4.2	46	1.3
30	12.	47	0.01
31	1.4		

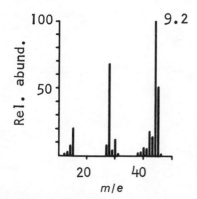

Unknown 9.3

m/e	Relative abundance	m/e	Relative abundance
14	2.0	32	1.2
15	4.7	33	0.22
18	0.3	41	1.0
19	3.0	42	3.3
25	2.1	43	8.4
26	9.3	44	1.7
27	23.	45	36.
28	4.7	46	16.
29	25.	47	0.45
30	6.0	48	0.03
31	100.		

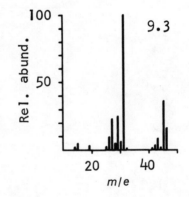

Unknown 9.4

m/e	Relative abundance	m/e	Relative abundance	m/e	Relative abundance	m/e	Relative abundance
15	2.1	52	0.38	78	0.48	121	0.61
28	2.7	63	2.3	91	3.2	122	1.0
30	1.4	64	2.1	92	12.	123	0.16
38	1.2	65	1.6	93	1.0	150	100.
39	1.3	66	0.30	104	32.	151	8.3
43	26.	74	4.0	105	2.4	152	0.96
44	0.64	75	6.0	106	0.22	165	18.
50	9.0	76	12.	119	1.1	166	1.7
51	2.9	77	3.8	120	6.5	167	0.19

9.4

Unknown 9.5

m/e	Relative abundance	m/e	Relative abundance
15	3.9	56	18.
16	0.16	57	100.
27	14.	58	4.3
28	3.8	59	0.07
29	27.	67	1.0
29.5 m	0.15	68	0.27
30	0.59	69	5.0
31.2 m	0.07	70	0.52
37.1 m	0.11	71	0.04
38	1.0	80	0.09
39	16.	81	0.77
40	2.5	82	0.13
41	41.	83	0.09
42	2.0	84	0.14
43	2.5	97	9.5
44	0.09	98	0.71
51	1.5	99	0.03
52	0.61	112	9.7
53	3.5	113	0.80
54	0.82	114	0.03
55	23.		

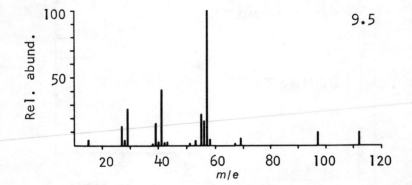

TABLE 9-1. *Infrared Correlation Chart* [a,b]

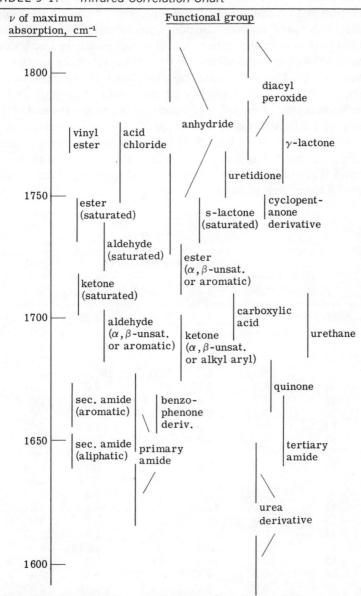

| ν of maximum absorption, cm^{-1} | Functional group |

Labels on chart:

1800

diacyl peroxide

vinyl ester

acid chloride

anhydride

γ-lactone

uretidione

1750

ester (saturated)

s-lactone (saturated)

cyclopentanone derivative

aldehyde (saturated)

ester (α, β-unsat. or aromatic)

ketone (saturated)

1700

aldehyde (α, β-unsat. or aromatic)

carboxylic acid

ketone (α, β-unsat. or alkyl aryl)

urethane

quinone

sec. amide (aromatic)

benzophenone deriv.

1650

sec. amide (aliphatic)

primary amide

tertiary amide

urea derivative

1600

[a] From Ref. *9.3*.

[b] Hydrogen bonding can reduce ν_{max} by as much as 75 cm^{-1}.

Unknowns 9.6 through 9.10 all have the same elemental composition and all contain the carbonyl group. Although the molecules are fairly simple, considerable difficulty is usually encountered in assigning structures to these, primarily because of the overlapping possibilities of the elemental compositions of particular peaks. (Of course high resolution information would simplify this.) The frequency of maximum absorption in the carbonyl region of the infrared spectrum is given at the end of the table to illustrate how a small amount of information from another source can often make interpretation of the mass spectrum much easier. Table 9-1 is a copy of an appropriate section of an infrared spectral correlation chart (*9.3*). Mass spectral data below *m/e* 24 have been omitted.

Unknowns 9.6–9.10

	Relative abundance				
m/e	9.6	9.7	9.8	9.9	9.10
25.2 m	0.07	—	—	0.20	—
26	3.8	5.5	5.7	11.	4.0
27	13.	40.	18.	37.	16.
28	4.1	6.3	12.	16.	8.1
29	25.	8.8	100.	100.	14.
30	1.3	0.25	1.3	4.0	1.5
31	1.7	1.3	2.6	7.2	2.3
32	0.08	0.09	0.22	0.32	1.3
33	—	0.06	—	1.1	0.06
37	—	1.7	1.7	0.26	0.52
37.1 m	—	—	—	0.04	—
38	—	2.9	2.4	0.26	0.53
39	—	15.	20.	0.79	1.6
40	0.08	2.4	3.9	0.24	0.67
41	0.66	42.	36.	3.1	3.0
42	5.9	11.	25.	3.1	3.0
43	100.	100.	58.	1.9	95.
44	2.8	3.8	91.	0.57	4.6
45	13.	13.	28.	5.0	100.
46	0.33	0.47	0.99	0.13	2.4
47	0.03	0.69	1.2	0.01	0.25
53	—	0.56	3.1	0.55	0.72
54	—	0.12	0.55	0.13	0.35

Unknowns 9.6–9.10 (Continued)

	Relative abundance				
m/e	9.6	9.7	9.8	9.9	9.10
55	0.07	3.8	3.5	3.4	1.9
56	—	0.35	0.50	2.4	0.45
56.0 m	0.51	—	—	—	—
57	0.04	0.20	1.8	75.	0.66
58	0.04	0.09	0.70	2.7	0.33
59	0.09	0.41	0.98	25.	0.38
60	0.61	2.1	1.9	0.95	2.6
61	9.9	0.62	2.8	0.26	0.12
62	0.22	—	0.30	—	—
63	0.04	—	0.62	—	—
67	—	—	3.0	—	0.11
68	—	0.07	2.1	—	0.03
70	4.7	0.38	33.	—	1.9
71	0.21	1.6	16.	0.07	0.41
72	—	0.15	1.4	—	2.3
73	3.0	21.	1.9	0.13	2.3
74	0.13	0.77	0.15	—	0.08
75	—	0.10	0.06	—	—
87	0.22	0.66	3.0	1.6	0.54
88	4.0	6.2	1.0	21.	6.9
89	0.24	0.35	0.05	1.03	0.38
90	0.02	0.05	—	0.12	0.05
Infrared (cm^{-1})					
	1745	1705	1660	1730	1705

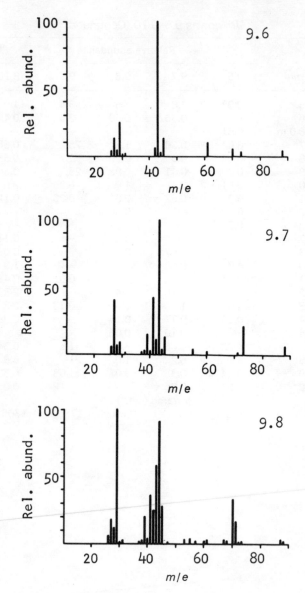

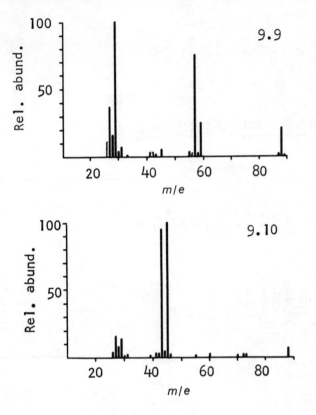

Unknowns 9.11 through 9.15 are further exercises.

Unknown 9.11

m/e	Relative abundance	m/e	Relative abundance	m/e	Relative abundance	m/e	Relative abundance
31	75.	65.5	0.81	87	3.3	118	1.5
32	0.84	66	3.4	88	0.03	119	0.05
35	9.1	67	0.08	93	13.	128	0.06
36	1.0	68	1.1	94	0.42	131	100.
37	2.8	69	74.	97	3.3	132	3.3
43	2.9	70	0.83	98	0.06	133	0.05
47	4.8	73.5	0.60	99	1.0	147	15.
48	0.05	74	4.1	100	0.84	148	0.05
49	1.5	75	0.16	109	0.41	149	4.7
50	6.9	78	1.1	111	0.12	150	0.33
51	0.10	81	10.	112	4.0	166	10.
55	2.4	82	0.27	113	0.14	167	0.37
62	5.1	85	10.	116	4.8	168	3.1
63	0.13	86	0.10	117	0.06	169	0.12

9.11

Unknown 9.12

m/e	Relative abundance	m/e	Relative abundance
13	2.0	45	100.
14	6.5	46	2.3
15	41.	47	3.5
28	2.8	48	0.06
29	46.	57	0.05
30	3.4	58	0.09
31	13.	59	0.09
32	0.83	60	0.02
33	0.23	61	0.01 *
43	0.96	75	44.
44	2.3	76	1.4
		77	0.19

* A real peak in the spectrum; not due to background.

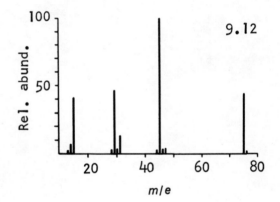

Unknown 9.13

m/e	Relative abundance	m/e	Relative abundance
27	2.0	64	2.6
28	0.59	65	27.
29	3.6	66	8.5
31	1.0	67	1.1
37	3.3	68	0.42
38	7.2	74	1.9
39	27.	75	1.4
40	6.6	76	19.
46	1.4	77	2.3
46.5	0.50	92	1.8
47	4.3	93	18.
50	5.4	94	5.8
51	3.4	95	0.39
52	0.77	104	13.
53	4.9	105	1.0
54	0.51	121	89.
55	1.6	122	100.
61	2.9	123	7.9
62	2.8	124	0.73
63	5.6		

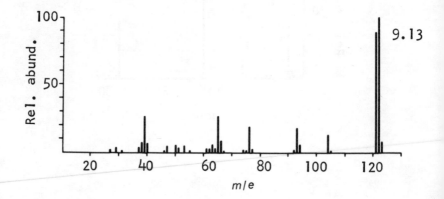

9.13

Unknown 9.14 is a minor component isolated from petroleum crude containing only carbon, hydrogen, and sulfur. A large number of low abundance (<1%) peaks have been omitted.

Unknown 9.15 is an amino acid isolated from a natural source as the ethyl ester.

9.6. Application of Mass Spectrometry to a Particular Field of Research

The practicing research scientist who has worked his way through this book will usually next test the applicability of mass spectrometry to his own field. An obvious approach is to obtain spectra of *known* key compounds that are typical of the field, and attempt to relate the spectra to the structures. Is the mass spectrum sensitive to the critical molecular features? If it is vital to know the position of aromatic substitution, other spectroscopic techniques are usually more effective (unless an "ortho effect" reaction is prominent — see Chapter 8). However, many unique capabilities of mass spectrometry should now be apparent, and interpretation of the actual spectra should show if there is such applicability to a particular field.

The student may get immediate opportunity for such practical application in his own research or in a course in qualitative organic analysis. If not, it is recommended that a number of more complex spectra be selected from the literature at random and interpreted. At this stage you should find the majority of the gross spectral features interpretable in a logical fashion. You may also discover the pleasure of finding new decomposition pathways to explain ions of unexpected abundance. The chemistry of unimolecular ion decomposition reactions is still in the early stages of exploration, and I hope you have come to share some of my excitement concerning its potential.

Unknown 9.14

m/e	Relative abundance	m/e	Relative abundance	m/e	Relative abundance	m/e	Relative abundance
39	12.	73.5	0.93	94.5	0.64	146	0.72
40	1.0	74	3.9	95	1.1	147	10.
41	2.2	75	4.2	96	0.17	148	1.2
44	0.59	76	3.1	101	1.1	149	0.62
45	10.	76.5	0.22	102	2.7	150	0.47
46	0.42	77	6.2	103	1.5	151	1.0
47	0.56	78	1.5	104	0.20	152	3.7
49	0.64	79	4.5	108	1.2	153	2.5
50	6.3	79.5	0.22	109	4.6	154	1.9
51	9.6	80	2.8	110	14.	155	0.78
52	1.8	80.5	0.40	111	1.5	158	3.0
53	1.8	81	1.5	112	0.77	159	5.3
57	1.3	82	2.3	113	1.3	160	100.
58	2.6	83	0.84	114	1.8	161	12.
59	1.6	84	2.4	115	21.	162	5.1
60	0.35	84.5	0.17	116	4.9	163	0.57
61	1.4	85	2.0	117	0.84	171	6.8
62	3.5	85.5	2.0	121	1.4	172	3.9
63	7.7	86	3.8	122	0.26	173	3.0
64	1.5	86.5	0.59	126	1.4	174	0.86
65	3.7	87	2.0	127	2.8	175	0.22
66	4.2	88	0.89	128	6.2	183	1.1
67	3.0	89	3.4	129	1.5	184	12.
67.5	0.30	90	0.97	130	0.22	185	8.9
68	0.36	91	2.5	134	5.2	186	6.0

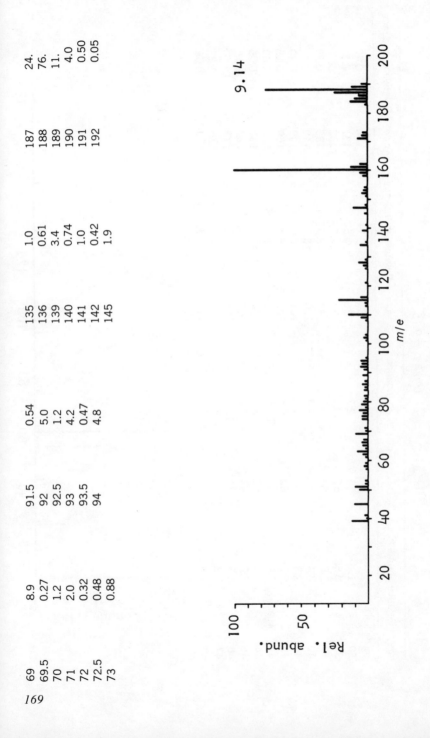

m/e	Rel. abund.
69	8.9
69.5	0.27
70	1.2
71	2.0
72	0.32
72.5	0.48
73	0.88

m/e	Rel. abund.
91.5	0.54
92	5.0
92.5	1.2
93	4.2
93.5	0.47
94	4.8

m/e	Rel. abund.
135	1.0
136	0.61
139	3.4
140	0.74
141	1.0
142	0.42
145	1.9

m/e	Rel. abund.
187	24.
188	76.
189	11.
190	4.0
191	0.50
192	0.05

9.14

Unknown 9.15

m/e	Relative abundance	m/e	Relative abundance	m/e	Relative abundance	m/e	Relative abundance
29	22.	54	2.4	85	0.71	130	0.42
30	11.	55	2.7	86	0.52	131	6.3
31	0.82	56	48.	87	2.2	132	0.36
39	1.8	57	5.1	88	3.5	133	0.28
40	0.41	58	1.2	100	5.6	148	3.2
41	2.3	59	1.8	101	0.62	149	0.20
42	6.7	60	0.82	102	5.4	150	0.15
43	7.9	61	100.	103	1.8	160	0.63
44	2.1	62	3.0	104	48.	161	0.05
45	6.2	63	4.3	105	2.6	162	0.16
46	4.9	74	12.	106	2.3	177	12.
47	5.3	75	8.0	114	1.1	178	1.2
48	1.6	76	0.59	116	3.9	179	0.66
49	1.3	83	2.1	129	6.1		

9.15

10

SOLUTIONS TO UNKNOWNS

(Instructions are given before Unknown 2.1.)

1.1. This is the mass spectrum of water. If any peak in the spectrum corresponds to the mass of the molecule (that is, molecular weight), this peak must be the one of highest mass. This spectrum, therefore, indicates that the sample has a molecular weight of 18. This molecule must contain elements of atomic weight no greater than that of oxygen, such as hydrogen, carbon, nitrogen, or oxygen, which have atomic weights of 1, 12, 14, and 16, respectively. An obvious combination is H_2O. This is confirmed by the peaks at masses 17 and 16 which represent the molecular fragments HO and O, respectively. [Water].

1.2. For this spectrum a molecular weight of 16 is indicated, which could correspond to CH_4. The other peaks in the spectrum support this, each of them corresponding to a carbon atom to which is attached a smaller number of hydrogen atoms. [Methane]

1.3. A molecular weight of 32 corresponds to two or less oxygen atoms. O_2 is ruled out, as its only possible fragment would have a mass of 16. The elemental composition CH_4O is indicated. The only possible arrangement for these is CH_3OH,

171

and the other peaks in the spectrum can all be justified as pieces of such a structure. [Methanol]

1.4. The knowledge that the main gaseous components of *air* are nitrogen, oxygen, and argon identifies the large 28, 32, and 40 peaks as N_2, O_2, and Ar, respectively. Masses 29, 33, and 34 are due to heavy isotopes of nitrogen and oxygen. The significance of such naturally occurring isotopes will be discussed later. Peaks at masses 14, 16, and 20 represent monoatomic and doubly charged species (for example, *m/e* of $Ar^{+2} = \frac{40}{2} = 20$). The ion of mass 44 is discussed in Unknown 1.5. [Nitrogen, oxygen, argon]

1.5. If the isotopic peaks of masses 45 and 46 are ignored, the base (largest) peak in the spectrum indicates a molecular weight of 44. The major peaks at 12 and 16 indicate that the compound contains carbon and oxygen and *m/e* 28 corresponds then to CO. Note that there are no peaks at masses 13, 14, and 15 which were indicative of CH_n groups in the spectra of CH_4 and CH_3OH. The formula of carbon dioxide does fit the observed peaks, with the *m/e* 22 corresponding to CO_2^{+2}. [Carbon dioxide]

1.6. Ignoring *m/e* 27 and 28 brings us to an indicated molecular weight of 26. The only apparent logical combination of atoms is C_2H_2, a fact which can be deduced from the presence of peaks at masses 12 (C_1) and 24 (C_2). Peaks at *m/e* 13 and 25 correspond to CH and C_2H, respectively, and the remaining small peaks contain heavy isotopes. [Acetylene]

1.7. [Hydrogen cyanide, Ref. *1.17*, no. 233]

1.8. [Fluoromethane, Ref. *1.17*, no. 968]

1.9. [Methanal, Ref. *1.17*, no. 84]

INSTRUCTIONS FOR SOLUTIONS TO THE UNKNOWNS.   As has been emphasized in other parts of this book, the most important way to learn how to interpret mass spectra is by actually working out structures from unknown spectra. Whether this book is used in a formal course or for self-instruction, it is important that the student work through a variety of unknown spectra. In attempting to solve a particular unknown, use the solution here only when you think you know the answer, or when you cannot go further. When you need help, use the solution given here only to get you past your particular difficulty and keep trying to arrive at your own answer. It is suggested that reference spectra *not* be used to solve these unknowns. These unknowns are designed to illustrate principles set forth in the text. Most are common molecules, so that little will be learned in locating them in a reference file of spectra that is properly indexed.

Follow *all* of the applicable steps of the outline, Table A-1, which you have covered in the text. (The first seven steps of the outline correspond to the first seven chapters.) The solutions will follow this order, although space limitations prohibit a discussion of every point for each unknown.

The spectra have been taken from the files of this laboratory or from the literature. The data have been corrected for contributions from impurities, ion-molecule reactions, and background, where such corrections appeared to be necessary. The abundances have been rounded off to two significant figures. Peaks of small abundance that were thought to be inconsequential to the solution of the spectrum have been omitted. This includes unimportant peaks below 1% (relative to the most abundant peak) at the low mass end of a group of peaks of unit mass separation, or at the low mass end of the spectrum.

2.1. (Be sure to note the instructions that precede this unknown.) This spectrum *could* indicate a molecule of mass 38 which could form an abundant fragment ion by the loss of two hydrogen atoms (m/e 36, $[M-2]^+$). The hints in the text should lead to the observation in Table A-2 of the 3/1 abundance ratio of the natural chlorine isotopes, masses 35 and 37. Thus, the spectrum is a mixture of HCl^{35} and HCl^{37}, in proportions corresponding to the isotopic abundances of Cl^{35} and Cl^{37}. [Hydrogen chloride]

2.2. The large peaks at masses 94 and 96 should arouse your suspicions, and a check of Table A-2 reveals that bromine has mass 79 and 81 isotopes of nearly equal abundances. The presence of bromine is supported by the fragment peaks of equal height (abundance) at m/e 79 and 81. Assuming that the mass 94 and 96 represent the molecular ions, by difference the molecule contains 15 mass units in addition to the bromine atom. There is support for this also in the spectrum at m/e 15. The smaller fragment ions at m/e 12–14 indicate the presence of CH_3, as do the ions of m/e 91–95. Note that there is some overlap here because of the bromine isotopes. Mass 94 is mainly CH_3Br^{79}, but contains an additional 2% $CHBr^{81}$. Peaks at masses 39.5–48 are due to doubly charged ions. [Methyl bromide]

2.3. In answer to the question in the text, if the mass 43 peak were due to $C_2H_3O^+$, the expected m/e 44/43 abundance ratio would be $2 \times 1.08\% = 2.16\%$ from the two C^{13} atoms present. Thus, the observed ratio corresponds more closely to that predicted for three carbon atoms, such as in the ion formula $C_3H_7^+$. However, one should always be aware of the possible contribution from "background" in the instrument, which is much more likely to give a high (not low — why?) indication of the number of carbon atoms. On the other hand, if an oxygen atom is present in the m/e 43 ion, there should be a 0.20% contribution to the m/e 45 peak due to $C_2H_3O^{18}$. The 0.05% contribution observed is mainly due to the $CC_2^{13}H_7$ and $C_2C^{13}H_6D$ ions.

To calculate the number of carbon atoms in the large m/e 58 peak, note that the abundance ratio of masses 59/58 is 4.39%. Using the formula of Table A-2 indicates 4 carbon atoms $(4.39\%/1.1\% \approx 4.0)$. The calculation for the $(M + 2)^+$ ion $(4.4^2/200)\% = 0.097\%$ is within the experimental error expected for the measurement of the small abundance of m/e 60. Thus, m/e 58 corresponds to C_4H_{10}, and the molecule is butane. The fact that this is the straight-chain isomer is not obvious from the spectrum with your present knowledge. Identities of major ions, such as masses 15 (CH_3^+) and 29 $(C_2H_5^+)$, should be obvious. [n-Butane, Ref. 1.17, no. 4]

2.4. You should suspect an isotopic cluster from the appearance of the mass 64 and 66 peaks. Note in Table A-2 that 5 common elements, O, Si, S, Cl, and Br have appreciable natural isotopes with a mass that is 2 units above the most abundant mass. Although the isotopic ratio of sulfur shown is not exactly matched by the relation of m/e 64/65/66 because of the contribution of other isotopes, the same ratio appears at 48/49/50 and 32/33/34 (and, qualitatively, at 24/24.5/25!). [Sulfur dioxide, Ref. 1.17, no. 97]

2.5. The striking feature of the isotopic ratios that you should note in this spectrum is the low $[M^+]/[M + 1^+]$ ratio and similar ion abundance ratios. Because of these ratios the elements C, O, Si, S, and Cl are all eliminated from consideration. Note that there are abundant peaks at $[M - 19]^+$ and $(M - 2 \times 19)^+$ as well as m/e 19 indicating the presence of fluorine. [Nitrogen trifluoride]

2.6. The isotopic cluster of m/e 62 and 64 should catch your eye immediately when you look at the bar graph. This sign-post for chlorine is repeated again, although less clearly, at other places in the spectrum such as m/e 48/50 and 35/37. The balance of the indicated molecular weight of 62 is then 27 (62 − 35). Several indications suggest the C_2H_3 to account for the mass 27 balance such as the mass 59–61 series (presence of at least 3 hydrogen atoms) and the mass 24–27 series (C_2^+-$C_2H_3^+$). [Vinyl chloride]

2.7. In the molecular ion region none of the abundance patterns appears to fit an "isotopic cluster" ratio. (Assigning the mass 66/68 ratio as O^{16}/O^{18} leaves a larger m/e 67 to account for.) The elemental composition formula of Table A-2 indicates 5 carbon atoms in m/e 66, that is, 5.6%/1.1% corresponds to $C_{5.0}$; $(5 \times 1.1\%)^2/200 = 0.15\%$ calculated for m/e 68 versus 0.18% found. Interferences reduce the significance of such calculations for other ions in the spectrum; for example, the mass 41/40 ratio indicates a maximum of 4 carbon atoms, $1.2/(28. \times 1.1\%) = 3.9$. The assumption of a C_5 formula for m/e 66 as the molecular ion can indicate a great deal about the structure of the molecule, however. Thus, the molecular formula must correspond to C_5H_6; $66 - (12 \times 5) = 6 \times 1$. Only a limited number of highly unsaturated hydrocarbons have this formula. A choice cannot be made between these with our present knowledge. [Cyclopentadiene]

2.8. Again no "isotopic cluster" is readily apparent in the molecular ion region. Applying the elemental composition formula of Table A-2 indicates 3 carbon atoms in the base peak at mass 72; 3.5%/1.1% corresponds to $C_{3.2}$. However, the check on the m/e 74/72 ratio reveals a discrepancy: $(3 \times 1.1\%)^2/200 = 0.05\%$, in comparison to the 0.48% found. Check the common isotopes of Table A-2 for an explanation. The C_3 accounts for only 36 amu of the molecular weight of 72. Both this difference and the m/e 74/72 ratio can be accounted for by assuming the presence of two oxygen atoms. For these there will be twice the probability that one of the oxygens of the molecule is an O^{18}. Thus, from the second formula of Table A-2 the m/e 74/72 ratio should be $0.05\% + 2 \times 0.20\% = 0.45\%$, checking the 0.48% found. The molecular formula $C_3H_4O_2$ is thus indicated. Similar calculations indicate $C_3H_3O^+$ for m/e 55 (loss of OH). Interferences prevent such calculations on other peaks (m/e 46/45 indicates a maximum of C_7). In interpreting the spectrum, the prominent m/e 27 must be C_2H_3 (it is far too abundant to be mass 54^{+2}). $C_3H_4O_2 - C_2H_3 = CO_2H$, suggesting (although not requiring) a carboxyl group as an assignment for the m/e 45. The only acid molecule of this composition is $CH_2{=}CHCOOH$. [Acrylic acid]

2.9. The molecular weight is 73. The highest mass peaks give no indication of isotopic clusters, but the possible error in the m/e 74 abundance limits any further calculations of elemental composition. However, m/e 58 should contain a maximum of 3 carbon atoms $(3.6\%/1.1\% = 3.3)$. Mass 60 supports this and also indicates no oxygen: $(3 \times 1.1)^2/200 = 0.05\%$. For the formula of m/e 58, there could be up to 7 hydrogen atoms associated with the 3 carbon atoms, accounting for 36 to 43 amu. The common elements (Table A-2) which can account for the 15 to 22 amu are now limited to H, N, and F. The highly unsaturated ion $C_3H_3F^+$ can be discarded in view of the rest of the spectrum (for instance, m/e 42 must then be $C_3H_6^+$). This makes $C_3H_8N^+$ the choice for m/e 58, and suggests $C_4H_{11}N^+$ for the molecular formula. (The difference of 15 amu is most likely CH_3, as removing an NH group from m/e 73 to yield m/e 58 would require multiple bond cleavage.) This formula corresponds to a saturated amine, and ways of differentiating these isomers will be discussed later. This is the spectrum of $(CH_3)_3$-CNH_2, which one might expect to show a strong tendency for loss of methyl. [*tert*-Butylamine]

3.1. $C_2H_4^{\ddagger}$, m/e 28; $C_3H_7O^+$, m/e 59; $C_4H_9N^{\ddagger}$, m/e 71; $C_4H_8NO^+$, m/e 86; $C_7H_5ClBr^+$, m/e 203; $C_6H_4OS^{\ddagger}$, m/e 124; $C_{29}F_{59}^+$, m/e 1469; H_3O^+, m/e 19; and $C_3H_9SiO^+$, m/e 89.

3.2. $C_{10}H_{15}O^+$ is an even-electron ion, and so cannot be the molecular ion.

3.3. $C_9H_{12}^{\ddagger}$ is an odd electron ion. The other ions represent losses of H, H_3 ($H + H_2$, for example), CH_3, $CH_3 + H_2$, and C_2H_5, respectively, all of which are possible losses. *n*-Propylbenzene would exhibit such a spectrum.

3.4. The presence of the large m/e 96 and 98 peaks casts doubt on the assignment of m/e 100 as the molecular ion. None of the common isotopes corresponds to this type of isotopic cluster, however. The ions of lower mass give helpful hints for elucidating this. Note particularly the m/e 63/61 ratio, the chlorine signpost. Formation of m/e 61 from m/e 96 involves the loss of 35 amu, a hint for a second chlorine atom in the molecule. The isotopic abundances of $Cl_2^{35}/Cl^{35}Cl^{37}/Cl_2^{37}$ should be (100%/ 32.7%)^2 = 100%/65.4%/10.7%; masses 96/98/100 are 100/64/10. To calculate the carbon content of M^+ from m/e 97/96, do not forget that the $Cl^{35}Cl^{37}$ isotopic ion of $(M-1)^+$ will contribute 65% of the m/e 95 to the 97 peak. $(3.3\% - 0.65 \times 3.0\%)/67\% \times 1.1\% = 1.8$ or $\sim C_2$. This calculation is superfluous, however, as the balance of molecular formula of 26 amu $(M^+ - Cl_2 = 96 - 70)$ is most logically due to C_2H_2. It is difficult to distinguish between the possible isomers of $C_2H_2Cl_2$ without standards. [*trans*-1,2-Dichloroethylene, Ref. *1.17*, no. 281]

3.5. The isotopic cluster at m/e 135–137 indicates one chlorine atom, and m/e 135 contains a maximum of 2 carbon atoms, $0.52/(1.1\% \times 24) = 2.0$. Similar assignments can be made for the lower mass ions: m/e 119, C_2Cl_0; m/e 100, C_2Cl_0; m/e 85, C_1Cl_1; m/e 69, C_1Cl_0; and m/e 50, C_1Cl_0. The absence of evidence for hydrogen atoms and the differences of 19 amu between several pairs of ions containing the same numbers of chlorine atoms implicate fluorine as the missing element. Thus, the formulas CF^+, CF_2^+, CF_3^+, $CClF_2^+$, $C_2F_4^+$, $C_2F_5^+$, and $C_2ClF_4^+$ will correspond in mass to the prominent peaks in the spectrum. You should have already noted that the m/e 135 and 137 peaks failed several of the requirements for a molecular ion. Because there is no indication of ions containing more than two carbon atoms or one chlorine atom, the most probable structure to account for this spectrum is $CClF_2CF_3$. [Chloropentafluoroethane]

3.6. [Nitromethane, Ref. *1.17*, no. 836]

3.7. [2,2-Dimethylpropane, Ref. *1.17*, no. 8]

3.8. [Ethanethiol, Ref. *1.17*, no. 79]

3.9. [Carbon tetrachloride, Ref. *1.17*, no. 603]

4.1. This spectrum is discussed in the text following the data on the unknown. [*n*-Hexadecane, Ref. *1.17*, no. 1005]

4.2. Calculating the number of carbon atoms from the m/e 507/506 ratio yields C_{30}, a formula which is misleading if the possible error is not appreciated. Actually, the similarity of the bar graph spectrum to that of *n*-hexadecane above should point to the *n*-alkane structure with the regular repeating pattern of 14 amu providing confirmation of the expected alkyl groups. [*n*-Hexatriacontane, Ref. *1.17*, no. 670]

4.3. The elemental composition indicated is C_6H_6, 6.4/ (100 × 1.1%), which corresponds to 4 rings + double bonds, $6 - (\frac{1}{2} \times 6) + (\frac{1}{2} \times 0) + 1$. The high abundance of this probable molecular ion also indicates a very stable molecule. A number of isomers are possible which could give the fragment ions shown; the energy required to fragment such stable structures also makes randomizing rearrangements possible. The ions of this spectrum are typically found in aromatic compounds, however. [Benzene, Ref. *1.17*, no. 250]

4.4. In calculating the elemental composition of m/e 182, correct the abundance of m/e 183 for the $(A + 2)^+$ contribution from the m/e 181 by assuming this is the same as m/e 184/182; $8.5 - (0.71 \times 8.2)/60 = 8.4$ (thus, the correction is relatively insignificant). Then $8.4/(1.1\% \times 60) = 12.7$ carbon atoms. The error in this figure depends on instrument reproducibility, but the accuracy is usually ±10%. Therefore, C_{12}, C_{13}, and C_{14} are possible, suggesting the formulas $C_{12}H_{22}O$, $C_{12}H_6O_2$, $C_{13}H_{26}$, $C_{13}H_{10}O$, and $C_{14}H_{14}$. For these, the m/e 184/182 ratios should be 1.07%, 1.37%, 1.02%, 1.22%, and 1.18%, respectively. These data do not allow a clear-cut decision, but the appearance of the spectrum strongly militates against the formula $C_{13}H_{26}$, and, to a lesser extent, $C_{12}H_{22}O$, both of which should have considerable resemblance to the aliphatic hydrocarbon pattern. Note the abundant peak that is probably the molecular ion, and the simplicity of the spectrum. The molecule should thus be generally stable, with one or a few bonds of much higher lability. Notice that there is a definite resemblance between the spectra of Unknowns 4.3 and 4.4—the peaks such as 39, 51, 63, and 77 suggest aromatic character. The possible formulas $C_{12}H_6O_2$, $C_{13}H_{10}O$, and $C_{14}H_{14}$ would have rings-plus-double-bonds values of 10, 9, and 8, respectively. With 4 per phenyl ring, the best possibilities for the mass 182 are $C_6H_5COC_6H_5$ and $(C_6H_5)_2C_2H_4$.

The 1,1 isomer of the latter should give a large $(M - CH_3)^+$ peak (m/e 167), and the 1,2 isomer a large $C_7H_7^+$ (m/e 91), neither of which is present. [Benzophenone]

4.5. Mass 86 appears to have the elemental composition $C_4H_6O_2$ (a better check with isotopic abundances than $C_5H_{10}O$), and for m/e 43 the formula $C_2H_3O^+$ is definitely preferable. Mass 15 should be CH_3^+. The appearance of the spectrum (that is, dominated by mass 43 and 15) suggests C_2H_3O and CH_3 groups that are readily lost. If the CH_3 is part of the C_2H_3O, the balance is CO. The absence of other peaks suggests a symmetrical structure, CH_3CO—$COCH_3$. Most other compounds of the formula $C_4H_6O_2$ would be expected to give some other fragments. The $(M - CH_3)^+$ is much smaller than CH_3^+ because of the electronegative groups on the concomitant —$COCOCH_3$ fragment. When the CH_3-CO bond is cleaved, the charge is preferably retained by the CH_3 group. [2,3-Butanedione, Ref. *1.17*, no. 782]

4.6. The isotopic abundances indicate the elemental compositions of C_7H_{15}, C_4H_9, C_3H_7, and C_2H_5 for prominent ions in the spectrum. Though small, the odd-electron ion at m/e 114 is probably the molecular ion, and the unknown is thus probably an octane, C_8H_{18}. Although CH_3^+, $C_2H_5^+$, $C_3H_7^+$, $C_4H_9^+$, and $(M - CH_3)^+$ are all important in the spectrum, the rule about relative importance with increased molecular weight would indicate that methyl and butyl groups are readily lost, but that ethyl and propyl are *not* readily lost: $(M - C_2H_5)^+$ and $(M - C_3H_7)^+$ are small. An octane corresponding to this is $(CH_3)_3CC$-$(CH_3)_3$. Reference spectra would be necessary to eliminate all other possibilities such as $(CH_3)_3CCH_2CH(CH_3)_2$.

Rearrangement peaks, such as $C_3H_7^+$ in this spectrum, are much more common in hydrocarbons than in many types of compounds. In this text hydrocarbon spectra are often used as illustrations despite this because their skeletons are fundamental to many other compounds encountered. [2,2,3,3-Tetramethylbutane, Ref. *1.17*, no. 56]

4.7. [Dibromomethane]

4.8. [1,2-Dihydroxyethane]

4.9. [3-Butenenitrile, Ref. *1.17*, no. 793]

4.10. [Pyrrole, Ref. *1.17*, no. 513]

5.1. The isotopic abundances indicate the elemental compositions C_7H_{15}, C_5H_{11}, C_4H_9, C_3H_7, and C_2H_5 for particular abundant ions. The odd-electron ion at m/e 128 is probably the molecular ion. Note that the mass series 15, 29, 43, 57, 71, 85, 99, and 113 is consistent with an alkyl ion series (Table A-4), and strongly favors the formula C_9H_{20} for the molecule even though the isotopic abundance determinations on m/e 128 (and m/e 113) cannot be made with sufficient accuracy to establish this formula. Taking into account the increasing importance of ion abundances with increasing mass, the molecule should show much more ready loss of C_2H_5 than n-nonane should show, and losses of CH_3 and C_4H_9 are roughly equivalent to the n-alkane. Any C_3H_7 groups must be much less labile than one or more C_2H_5 groups. The isomeric nonane possibilities cannot be narrowed to only one on this basis, but many can be eliminated. [3,5-Dimethylheptane, Ref. 1.17, no. 343]

5.2. Although the possible molecular ion at m/e 128 probably has the composition $C_{10}H_8$, a C_9 formula cannot be ruled out on the basis of isotopic abundances. However, any resemblance to the nonane spectrum of Unknown 5.1 stops at this point. The probable molecular ion is of high stability; there are few fragment peaks of importance; and these resemble the aromatic series (Table A-4). (The large M^{+2} is also typical of aromatics.) The formula $C_{10}H_8$ requires 7 rings-plus-double-bonds ($10 - \frac{8}{2} + 1$). Again reference spectra would be necessary to distinguish between the several isomers possible. [Naphthalene, Ref. 1.17, no. 410]

5.3. The m/e 61 peak is probably due to heavy isotope contributions from m/e 60; m/e 60, however, is too large to be due to isotopic contributions from the common elements, and thus should be suspected as the odd-electron molecular ion. Mass 45 should contain 2 (or less) carbon atoms, but isotope calculations for m/e 31 are thwarted by its relatively small size and the O_2 background contribution to m/e 32. (The m/e 32 datum was omitted for these reasons.) The most significant ion series of the spectrum is that of masses 31, 45, and 59. (The series 15, 29, 43 and 27, 41 are less indicative as they can arise by losses of small molecules from the 31, 45, 59 series.) Table A-4 suggests $C_nH_{2n+1}O$ from alcohols or ethers for this series; from Table A-3 alcohols would be suspected to have M^+ abundances corresponding to the low abundance of m/e 60. Only two isomers are possible; as will be discussed in detail later, the sizable $(M - 1)^+$ and $(M - 15)^+$ peaks strongly indicate $(CH_3)_2CHOH$. [Isopropanol, Ref. *1.17*, no. 285]

5.4. Again the molecular weight is apparently 60, and the formula contains three carbon atoms or less. The spectrum is dominated, however, by m/e 30, which is either an odd-electron ion, or contains an odd number of nitrogen atoms. This could also be viewed as part of the series 16, 30, 44, but in either case Table A-4 makes the grouping $—CH_2NH_2$ a prime suspect. The formula for mass 60 should now be $C_2H_8N_2$, for which the isomer $H_2NCH_2CH_2NH_2$ is the best choice because of the appreciable $(M - 1)^+$ and $(M - NH_2)^+$ peaks, and lack of $(M - CH_3)^+$. [1,2-Diaminoethane]

5.5. The indicated molecular ion, m/e 178, could have a variety of compositions of 13 to 15 carbon atoms. The huge $M^{+\cdot}$ peak and the large M^{+2} peak are consistent with the indication of aromatic character given by the series of ions m/e 39, 50, 51, 52, 63, and so on. Loss of C_2H_2 is typical of aromatic molecules. Several isomers of $C_{14}H_{10}$ (rings-plus-double-bonds = 10) are possible, and again reference spectra are necessary to distinguish between the isomers. The higher energy processes involved in the decompositions of such molecules make rearrangements much more probable. [Diphenylacetylene]

5.6. There are a number of signs that this compound is quite different from the preceding ones. Masses 76, 69, 50, 31, and 26 have a maximum of 2, 1, 1, 1, and 1 carbon atoms, respectively. Mass 95 is either *not* the molecular ion, or else has an odd number of nitrogen atoms. Similarly, prominent ions of m/e 76, 50, and 26 are either odd-electron fragment ions, or contain an odd number of nitrogen atoms. There are few or no hydrogen atoms present (no groups of peaks in unit mass sequence, as 66, 67, 68, 69). The practiced eye may have found a valuable clue in the ion series of masses 31, 50, and 69 (see Table A-4). The lack of hydrogens even makes the low mass peaks of 12, 14, and 19 serve as clues to the atoms present. Assuming m/e 95 to be the molecular ion gives correspondence between ions at masses 19 and $M - 19$, and at 26 and $M - 26$, suggesting the parts $F—CF_2—CN$. [Trifluoroacetonitrile]

5.7. If m/e 130 is the molecular ion, the number of carbon atoms is quite small (5 or less) for this high mass. Therefore m/e 129 is a much better candidate to be the molecular ion, which would mean the molecule contains an odd number of nitrogen atoms. The abundant ions of even mass such as 102, 98, and 78 could in this way be even-electron ions. The high abundance of this postulated molecular ion would also be consistent with the aromatic-type ion series. Again several isomers are possible of the formula C_9H_7N (rings-plus-double-bonds = 7), and reference spectra would give positive identification. [Isoquinoline, Ref. *1.17*, no. 626].

5.8. A relatively abundant $(M-2)^+$ ion is unusual in mass spectra, so the 164/166 should be checked out as a possible isotopic cluster. One bromine atom is indicated by a number of such ion pairs. The ion series m/e 15, 29, 43, 57, 71, and 85 indicates alkyl to C_6, or possibly carbonyl to C_5. The bromine-containing ion series m/e 79–81, 93–95, 107–109, 121–123, and 135–137 gives strong support to the presence of the alkyl chain, and to the formula $C_6H_{13}Br$ for the m/e 164–166 ions. Unfortunately, the presence of the CH_2Br^+ ion cannot be taken as proof that this is a 1-bromoalkane, as small amounts of CH_2Br^+ are formed by rearrangement in the spectra of some alkanes in which the bromine atom is not terminally substituted. Later discussion will point out that the large m/e 135–137 ions strongly indicate the isomeric identity. [1-Bromohexane]

6.1. "Metastable" peaks are indicated at m/e 24.1, 25.1, 30.4, 31.9, 35.1, 37.1, and 39.2. (Narrow peaks at fractional masses are due to multiply charged ions.) Probable transitions are: 24.1, $28^+ \rightarrow 26^+ + 2$; 25.1, $29^+ \rightarrow 27^+ + 2$; 30.4, $58^+ \rightarrow 42^+ + 16$; 31.9, $58^+ \rightarrow 43^+ + 15$; 35.1, $39^+ \rightarrow 37^+ + 2$; 37.1, $41^+ \rightarrow 39^+ + 2$; 39.2, $43^+ \rightarrow 41^+ + 2$. [*n*-Butane]

6.2. Acetic acid could possibly give the major ions of Figure 6-2; m/e 60, 59, 45, and 43 could correspond to M^+, $(M-1)^+$, $COOH^+$, and CH_3CO^+, respectively. However, the "metastable peak" at 24.1 corresponds to the transition $28^+ \rightarrow 26^+ + 2$. This evidence along with the peaks of probable composition $C_2^+–C_2H_3^+$ eliminates the possibility of acetic acid. Additionally the following decomposition reactions which are indicated by metastables would be unlikely for CH_3COOH: $60^+ \rightarrow 44^+ +$

16 (m/e 32.2), $59^+ \rightarrow 41^+ + 18$ (m/e 28.5), and $45^+ \rightarrow 29^+ + 16$ (m/e 18.7, flat-topped). Note that m/e 16.2 might be due to either $59^+ \rightarrow 31^+ + 18$ or $45^+ \rightarrow 27^+ + 18$. [Isopropanol]

6.3. Mass 60 may be the molecular ion; it appears to have a maximum of three carbon atoms. Note the abundant odd-electron ion at m/e 42. A significant feature of the spectrum is the ion series of masses 31, 45, 59, indicative of an alcohol (see discussion of Unknown 5.3). This is borne out by the m/e 42 $(M - H_2O)^{+}$, for which Table A-5 suggests primary alcohols. Compare this spectrum to isopropanol, Unknown 5.3, especially noting the $(M - CH_3)^+$, $(M - H_2O)^{+}$, and $(M - C_2H_5)^+$ peaks. [*n*-Propanol, Ref. *1.17*, no. 284]

6.4. Again m/e 60 is indicated as the molecular weight, but it appears to contain less than three carbon atoms, and the m/e 62/60 ratio suggests 2 oxygen atoms. Note the abundant odd-electron ion at m/e 32. This is *not* air background—m/e 28 is much too small (see Unknown 1.4). Also m/e 32 is probably not an even-electron ion with one nitrogen atom—it is hard to formulate nitrogen in a plausible ion of this mass. There is no clear-cut indication of an even-electron ion series of low mass. The m/e 32 corresponds to the $(M - 28)^{+}$ ion; Table A-5 suggests this can be due to the loss of C_2H_4 or CO. Either must be a re-arrangement, and such reactions will be discussed in detail later. The 33/32 ratio (and the low tendency of O_2 to retain the positive charge) suggests that m/e 32 is actually CH_4O^+ (loss of CO). The base peak at m/e 31 must be due to $-CH_2OH$ or $-OCH_3$; the latter is indicated by the abundance of m/e 15. Fitting these pieces together gives $HCOOCH_3$. [Methyl formate, Ref. *1.17*, no. 383]

6.5. Again the molecular formula appears to be $C_2H_4O_2$, but the spectrum is dominated by $(M - 15)^+$ and $(M - 17)^+$. Table A-5 suggests these to be losses of CH_3 and OH, respectively, indicating CH_3COOH. The relatively small peak at m/e 31 may be misleading—it is caused by the rearrangement loss of CO plus one hydrogen atom. [Acetic acid, Ref. *1.17*, no. 640]

7.1. Mass 100 is indicated as the molecular ion, but the m/e 101/100 ratio suggests an improbable maximum of 8 carbon atoms. Masses 72, 57, and 43 appear to have maxima of 4, 4, and 2 carbon atoms, respectively. If no nitrogen is present, m/e 72 must be an odd-electron ion. The most striking ion series is m/e 29, 43, 57 (71 – missing), and 85, for which Table A-4 suggests alkyl and (or) aliphatic carbonyl (or cyclic ether). The molecular composition $C_6H_{12}O$ and possibly the structure $CH_3COC_4H_9$ could be postulated from the m/e 43 and 57 carbon-content maxima. Such a tenuous hypothesis is greatly strengthened by study of the dominant odd-electron m/e 72 fragment ion. For $(M - 28)^+$ ions Table A-5 indicates common losses of CO or C_2H_4, with the latter borne out by the carbon composition. Table A-7 indicates R—CO—CHR'—Z—H (in this case Z = —C_2H_4—) or CHR=CR'O—Z—H, where R + R' = C_2H_5. (The other two structural possibilities shown are eliminated because the ion is formed by loss of C_2H_4.) The large $C_2H_3O^+$ ion militates against the structure CHR=CR'O—Z—H, and suggests that R—CO—CHR'—Z—H is actually CH_3—CO—CH(CH_3)-C_2H_4—H. [3-Methyl-2-pentanone, Ref. *1.17*, no. 663]

7.2, 7.3, 7.4. These appear to be isobars of molecular weight 120. The possible error in the m/e 121/120 ratio makes it difficult to distinguish between C_9 and C_8, although the m/e 122/120, 107/105, and 106/105 ratios give preference to C_8H_8O for Unknown 7.3 and to C_9H_{12} for the other two. Rings-plus-double-bonds are thus either 5 or 4. There are many other signs in the spectrum that all three compounds are aromatic. "Mass Spectral Correlations" (*1.15*) suggests the phenyl moiety in compounds giving sizable m/e 77 peaks, benzyl for m/e 91, and either $CH_3C_6H_4CH_2$—, $C_6H_5CH(CH_3)$—, or C_6H_5CO— for m/e 105. The spectrum of Unknown 7.4 can therefore be explained by the structure $C_6H_5CH_2CH_2CH_3$ – the abundance of the $C_7H_7^+$ ion produced by benzylic bond cleavage is not surprising in light of the chemistry of such compounds, and the lower loss of CH_3 would also be expected. For Unknowns 7.2 and 7.3, a number of compounds of molecular weight 120 could give large losses of CH_3: $CH_3C_6H_4CH_2CH_3$, $C_6H_5CH(CH_3)_2$, and $C_6H_5COCH_3$. Even $C_6H_3(CH_3)_3$ cannot safely be eliminated without reference standards. The large m/e 77 indicates the C_6H_5-containing compounds, although the m/e 79 rearrangement ion (to be discussed later) of Unknown 7.2 gives little confidence in this reasoning for this molecule. The very small losses of hydrogen (masses 119, 118, 104, 103) of Unknown 7.3 compared to the others indicate $C_6H_5COCH_3$ in confirmation of the elemental composition data. The $(M - 15)^+/M^+$ ratio of Unknown 7.2 supports the structure $C_6H_5CH(CH_3)_2$ (the structure $CH_3C_6H_4$-C_2H_5 has fewer benzylic methyls), but reference spectra would be necessary to establish this firmly. [Isopropylbenzene, acetophenone, and *n*-propylbenzene]

8.1, 8.2, 8.3. Discussed in the text. Note that Unknown 8.3 is the same as Unknown 4.6. Was it easier this time?

8.4, 8.5, 8.6. The $C_nH_{2n+1}^+$ ion series is strongly indicated, and its distribution should suggest the *n*-alkane $C_{16}H_{34}$ as the compound yielding spectrum *8.4*. (You also saw this spectrum as Unknown 4.1.) Several of the prominent $C_nH_{2n+1}^+$ ions of Unknowns 8.5 and 8.6 appear paired with a $C_nH_{2n}^+$ ion; loss of (R + H) is also a common decomposition reaction for a compound with an R alkyl branch. Thus in Unknown 8.5 the ions of m/e 211, 168–169, 140–141 (weak), and 84–85 indicate chain branchings corresponding to C_1—C_{15}, C_4—C_{12}, C_6—C_{10}, and C_{10}—C_6. The grouping *n*-C_4H_9—$CH(CH_3)$— will explain these data. The compound is actually $CH_3(CH_2)_3CH(CH_3)(CH_2)_9$-$CH_3$, although the compound $CH_3(CH_2)_3CH(CH_3)(CH_2)_4$-$CH(CH_3)(CH_2)_3CH_3$ also should give similar prominent alkyl ions. For Unknown 8.6 the ions of m/e 182–183, 140–141, and 85 are abundant in comparison to the spectrum of *n*-$C_{16}H_{34}$, indicating branches corresponding to C_3—C_{13}, C_6—C_{10}, and C_{10}—C_6. A first postulate to fit these data might be the C_3H_7-—$CH(C_2H_5)$— group, but this is made improbable by the low abundance of $(M - C_2H_5)^+$, that is, the *negative* information that there is no appreciable loss of C_1, C_2, C_4, or C_5 is very valuable. The data can be fitted by $CH_3(CH_2)_5CH(n$-$C_3H_7)(CH_2)_5$-CH_3. [*n*-Hexadecane, 5-methylpentadecane, and 7-*n*-propyltridecane, Ref. *1.3*, p. 79]

8.7. Your suspicions concerning the m/e 148–150 doublet can be confirmed at masses 119–121, 105–107, 91–93 and 77–79; this is the chloroalkyl ion series. Isotopic abundances indicate the $C_nH_{2n+1}^+$ ion series as another important feature of the spectrum, consistent with the elemental composition $C_8H_{17}Cl$ for m/e 148 as the molecular ion. Strong peaks at $C_7H_{15}^+$ and

$C_4H_9^+$ suggest cleavage at chain branching enhanced through electron withdrawal by the chlorine atom (the abundance of the $C_4H_9^+$ can be viewed as arising through ionization of the most labile bond, with the charge going to the least electronegative fragment). $(M - C_2H_5)^+$ is the prominent ion in the chloroalkyl series. The abundant ions discussed are consistent with the structure $ClCH_2CH(C_2H_5)(CH_2)_3CH_3$. [3-(Chloromethyl)-heptane]

8.8, 8.9, 8.10. Note that alkylphenols are among the few common types of molecules which would account for the ions formed at lower molecular weights. To elucidate the nature of the alkyl substitution, only the $(M - C_nH_{2n+1})^+$ ions need be considered. For Unknown 8.8, $(M - CH_3)^+$ dominates this series. This can only mean that there are many more benzylic methyl groups than any other such substituent; the compound is actually the di-*tert*-butyl isomer, although the *tert*-butyltetramethyl isomer could behave similarly. The $(M - alkyl)^+$ ion series of Unknown 8.9 is dominated by the $(M - C_2H_5)^+$ ion, suggesting a number of structures with multiple ethyl substitution on a carbon atom adjacent to the benzene ring. The small amount of $(M - CH_3)^+$ peak is actually significant in this case, however, as benzylic loss of C_2H_5 is heavily favored over the benzylic loss of the smaller CH_3. The compound is actually the di-*sec*-butyl isomer. (The loss of C_2H_5 is much more abundant than loss of CH_3 even in *sec*-butyl-*tert*-butylphenol.) Finally, Unknown 8.10 indicates almost no alkyl loss smaller than C_5H_{11}, which loss yields the largest peak found in the spectrum. This peak indicates HO—phenyl—C—C_5H_{11}, to which must be added two methyl groups. The structure is actually HO—C_6H_4—$C(CH_3)_2$—$CH_2C(CH_3)_3$, so that the 0.21% $(M - CH_3)^+$ ion represents the benzylic methyl cleavage of two CH_3 groups in competition with the large C_5H_{11} group. The significant m/e 107 gives indication of the α,α'-dimethyl substitution, as loss of C_2H_4 is expected from the ion Y—phenyl—$C(CH_3)_2^+$. The preponderance of $C_4H_9^+$ among the alkyl ions of the spectrum is consistent with the terminal *tert*-butyl group. For these compounds, changing the position of substitution on the benzene ring makes relatively small changes in the spectra. [di-*tert*-Butylphenol, di-*sec*-butylphenol, 1,1,3,3-tetramethylbutylphenol]

8.11 through 8.17. Unknown 8.11 was discussed as Unknown 2.9, and Unknown 8.12 is identified in the text. Although the information is given that these are isomeric C_4-amines, note that determination of the elemental composition of M^+ would be high in several cases using the m/e 74/73 ratio. This is mainly due to the production of $(M + 1)^+$ by an ion-molecule reaction (see Section 3.3).

In answer to the question in the text, loss of an α-methyl group is in competition with the losses of other α substituents. The probability of α-CH_3 loss is much greater than α-H loss, but less than α-C_2H_5 loss. This helps to identify Unknown 8.17 as $C_2H_5CH(CH_3)NH_2$. Of the 5 α-CH_3 amines listed (see text), only $(CH_3)_2CHNHCH_3$ and $CH_3CH_2N(CH_3)_2$ remain unidentified; the first should have a larger $(M - CH_3)^+/M^+$ ratio, and so is Unknown 8.15. The assignment of the latter structure to Unknown 8.16 is borne out by the m/e 44 of this spectrum; it is formed by the elimination of C_2H_4 from the $(M - 1)^+$ ion through a rearrangement similar to the formation of m/e 30 in $C_2H_5NHC_2H_5$ (see Section 8.5).

The remaining possible isomers are $CH_3CH_2CH_2CH_2NH_2$, $(CH_3)_2CHCH_2NH_2$, and $CH_3CH_2CH_2NHCH_3$. The first two should yield abundant ions of m/e 30, and are thus Unknowns 8.13 and 8.14. These spectra are surprisingly similar, reflecting the dominant effect of the amine function on the cleavage; however, the small absolute differences in the abundances of the alkyl ions are reproducible and significant. The abundances of the $C_3H_7^+$ and $C_4H_9^+$ ions in Unknown 8.15 are several times the corresponding abundances in Unknown 8.14 (only small contributions should be present from $C_2H_5N^+$ and $C_3H_7N^+$), compatible with *n*- and isobutylamine assignments for 8.14 and 8.15, respectively. No spectrum is given for *n*-$C_3H_7NHCH_3$; it should give a base peak at m/e 44, but an insignificant peak at $(M - CH_3)^+$. [8.11, *tert*-Butylamine; 8.12, diethylamine; 8.13, *n*-butylamine; 8.14, isobutylamine; 8.15, isopropylmethylamine; 8.16, ethyldimethylamine; and 8.17, *sec*-butylamine]

8.18. Elemental composition determinations are inaccurate because of interferences and low relative abundances. Mass 130 appears to be a good possibility for the molecular ion, however, and the ion series 31, 45, 59, 73, 87, 101, and 115 strongly suggests that the molecular formula is $C_8H_{18}O$. Table A-3 shows that the abundance of M^+ is indicative of an ether, not an alcohol. Facile cleavage of C_α-C_β bonds should yield the most abundant $C_nH_{2n+1}O^+$ ions; the $(M - 43)^+$ is the most abundant of these by far, and thus indicates one or two propyl groups substituted on one or both α-carbon atoms. The abundances of $(M - CH_3)^+$ and $(M - C_2H_5)^+$ are roughly 3% and 10%, respectively, of $(M - C_3H_7)^+$, making the presence of methyl or ethyl substituents on an α-carbon atom unlikely, although comparison with spectra of similar compounds would be necessary to evaluate these effects quantitatively. The other common decomposition of ethers via cleavage of the C-O bond to yield the alkyl ion strongly indicates a butyl ether (m/e 57); of course $C_8H_{18}O$ must then be a dibutyl ether. The formula $C_3H_7CH_2OC_4H_9$ is required; $C_3H_7CH_2OCH(CH_3)C_2H_5$ is less probable because of the abundances of $(M - CH_3)^+$ and $(M - C_2H_5)^+$, as discussed. [Diisobutyl ether]

$$C_3H_7-CH_2OC_4H_9 \xrightarrow{-e^-} \begin{cases} C_3H_7-CH_2\overset{+\cdot}{O}\,C_4H_9 \rightarrow C_3H_7{}^\circ + CH_2{=}\overset{+}{O}C_4H_9 \\ C_3H_7-CH_2\overset{+\cdot}{O}|C_4H_9 \rightarrow C_3H_7CH_2O\cdot + C_4H_9^+ \end{cases}$$

8.19. The abundant m/e 98 may be the molecular ion; isotope ratios indicate $C_6H_{10}O$ for it, consistent with the carbonyl band in the infrared spectrum. Rings-plus-double-bonds $= 2$, or 1 in addition to the carbonyl group. Isotope ratios definitely indicate that m/e 43 is *not* $C_3H_7^+$, so that the alkyl ion series is limited to C_2 at most. The 27, 41, 55 (69 – missing), 83 ion series suggests alkenes or cycloalkanes, consistent with the rings-plus-double-bonds calculation, *and (or)* alkenyl- or cycloalkylcarbonyl, consistent with the rings-plus-double-bonds calculation and the infrared spectrum. The abundance of m/e 43 strongly suggests the acetyl group, which would also account for the abundant $(M - CH_3)^+$. The other group attached to the carbonyl must have the formula C_4H_7. The comparable abundances of $C_4H_7^+$ and CH_3CO^+ indicate equivalent capabilities for stabilizing the positive charge. [4-Methyl-3-penten-2-one, Ref. *1.17,* no. 381]

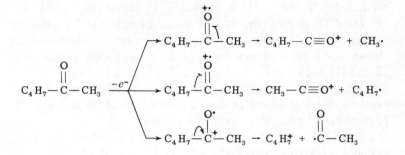

8.20, 8.21, 8.22. All of these molecules appear to have the molecular formula C_3H_6O, and thus contain one ring or double bond. One approach that is often valuable is to record all likely isomers, and predict their spectra (this approach can be applicable for complex molecules when other information has eliminated many structural possibilities). For C_3H_6O the following molecules are possible:

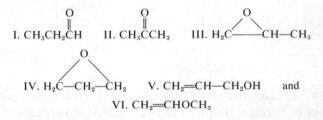

We have not discussed spectra of the cyclic compounds as yet; their molecular ions have increased stability because of the ring system, although the ring can complicate the interpretation of their spectra.

In compound I a large m/e 29 peak should result from α cleavage, no matter which fragment retains the charge; α cleavage should give $(M - H)^+$ in less abundance. These are the predominant features of Unknown 8.20. The m/e 28 is probably formed by the rearrangement loss of formaldehyde. Unknown 8.21 is dominated by the $(M - 1)^+$ ion; this indicates strong activation of a hydrogen atom and that there is no other labile group in the molecule. IV has four α-hydrogen atoms, but the formation of the $(M - 18)^+$ from IV would require considerable rearrangement. In V the α-H is activated by both the —OH and —CH=CH₂ groups; the m/e 31 would be expected by cleavage of the C_α—C_β adjacent to the —OH group. Unknown 8.22 shows a strong tendency for loss of methyl; only compounds II and III are consistent with this. Without a knowledge of the spectra of cyclic compounds it is difficult to eliminate III *a priori;* actually, the largest peak in the spectrum of III is at m/e 28. [Propionaldehyde, allyl alcohol, acetone]

8.23. The retro Diels–Alder reactions expected for these isomers are shown here. The low abundance of m/e 164 in the second spectrum is due to the competition of the loss of CH_3 by the allylic cleavage that is possible for this isomer. [α-Ionone, β-ionone, Ref. *8.14*]

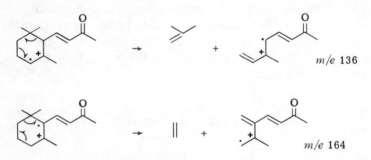

8.24. If mass 101 is the molecular ion, it must contain an odd number of nitrogen atoms. The $(M - CH_3)^+$ ion appears to have no more than 4 carbon atoms, and m/e 59 to have 2 carbon atoms and no more than one oxygen atom. Any even-electron ion series of Table A-4 that includes m/e 59 is ruled out by the isotopic abundances. In fact, the identity of this ion fragment is a major key to the identity of Unknown 8.24. With a maximum of C_2 and O_1, and with the indicated presence of nitrogen, the formula C_2H_5NO is a logical postulate for m/e 59, and is an *odd-electron ion,* $(M-42)^+$. Table A-7 suggests H_2NCOCH_2—Z—H or $HON=CHCH_2$—Z—H; for Z, 42 amu, Table A-5 suggests C_3H_6 or CH_2CO. Corresponding to these, the prominent $(M - 15)^+$ and m/e 43 peaks suggest either —CH(CH₃)₂ or —COCH₃ as terminal groups. The former is indicated by the mass 88/86 ratio, but the accuracy of this is doubtful. Differentiation between the possible amide and oxime structures also requires study of reference spectra of similar compounds. [3-Methylbutyramide]

8.25. The apparent molecular ion at m/e 134 contains 10 ± 1 carbon atoms and probably no oxygen atoms. Thus $C_{10}H_{14}$ is a favorable postulate, with rings-plus-double-bonds = 4. The odd-electron ion at m/e 92 is especially noteworthy. There is some indication of an alkyl ion series (m/e 15, 29, 43), but the most striking is the aromatic ion series. This is borne out by the rings-plus-double-bonds value and the abundant doubly charged ions. A logical postulate for the unknown is thus a C_4-benzene; the abundant m/e 92 (Table A-7) indicates the structure is $C_6H_5CH_2$—C_3H_7. The low abundance ratio of m/e 43/29 indicates the alkyl chain is not branched. [*n*-Butylbenzene]

8.26. If one remembers that abundant $(M - 2)^{\ddagger}$ peaks are uncommon, the mass 146–148 appearance should suggest an isotopic cluster. The most probable suspects of Table A-2 are silicon and sulfur. One atom of sulfur fits the mass 148/146 ratio better, and this postulation leaves a residual at m/e 147 indicating roughly 9 carbon atoms (correspondingly, Si_1 would indicate roughly C_5). Sulfur (or silicon) is also indicated in m/e 89, but not in masses 112, 98, or 84. Assuming that m/e 146 is the molecular ion and contains no nitrogen atoms, a series of abundant *odd-electron* ions is apparent: masses 42, 56, 70, 84, 98, and 112. Table A-7 suggests an olefin ion series; the abundant $(M - 34)^{\ddagger}$ and $(M - 62)^{\ddagger}$ indicate a thiol. This is supported by the alkyl ion series and by the m/e 47, 61, 75, 89, 103 ion series. Mass 89, the most abundant ion of these, corresponds to the cyclic ion formed in *n*-alkyl mercaptans. [*n*-Octyl mercaptan]

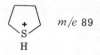

m/e 89

8.27. Mass 178 can be postulated as the molecular ion, with roughly 12 carbon atoms. Both m/e 105 and 123 appear to contain 7 carbon atoms. The m/e 122 is of questionable significance as an odd-electron ion because of the abundant m/e 123 ion; however the mass 56 peak, $(M - 122)^{\ddagger}$, should be noted. A weak alkyl ion series through C_4 is present, as is an aromatic ion series. There are weak alkyl loss ions at $(M - 15)^+$, $(M - 29)^+$, and $(M - 43)^+$, but instead of $(M - 57)^+$ there are the major ions at $(M - 55)^+$ and $(M - 56)^{\ddagger}$. From Table A-5 a common loss of 55 is loss of C_4H_7 from esters (double hydrogen rearrangement) and the loss of 56 would be the rearrangement loss of C_4H_8 from carbonyl compounds. The abundant m/e 56 odd-electron ion supports this; Table A-7 indicates a corresponding C_4H_8—RY structure. Two other abundant ions provide the final clues; m/e 77 and 105 should be phenyl and benzoyl, suggesting that the compound is a butyl benzoate. This is probably not *sec-* or *tert*-butyl; for example, $(M - 15)^+$ and $(M - 29)^+$ are less abundant than $(M - 43)^+$. [*n*-Butyl benzoate]

8.28. The m/e 99/98 ratio is suspiciously large for m/e 98 to be the molecular ion; the m/e 84 makes m/e 99 a much more likely candidate. This suggests that the molecule contains an odd number of nitrogen atoms, and makes difficult the identification of the odd-electron ions of the spectrum. The m/e 59, 45, and 31 ions appear to contain 3, 2, and 1 carbon atoms, respectively. Assuming that the m/e 84 ion contains one nitrogen atom, the 85/84 ratio indicates 4 carbon atoms. The significant mass 31, 45, and 59 ions suggest (Table A-4) an alcohol or ether functionality, but the possibility of nitrogen demands consideration of C_2H_5NO (Table A-7) for m/e 59. This dilemma can be resolved if the nitrogen functionality can be pin-pointed, and the anomalous m/e 54 gives a strong indication of this. Table A-4 suggests —C_2H_4CN, and the presence of a nitrile group would also explain the unusual $(M - 1)^+$ and $(M - 27)^+$ ions. The m/e 59 ion is most likely $HOC(CH_3)_2$—, $CH_3OCH(CH_3)$—, or $C_2H_5OCH_2$—, in light of $(M - 15)^+ >> (M - 29)^+$. The only one of these compatible with the base peak at mass 31 is $C_2H_5OCH_2$—. (This is a difficult unknown because of the two functional groups and the isobaric possibilities for a number of the ions. Obviously some additional information would greatly simplify the solution, for example, the infrared spectrum defining the presence of a nitrile group.) [β-Cyanoethyl ethyl ether]

$$CH_3 CH_2 \overset{+\cdot}{O} CH_2 CH_2 CN \ \rightarrow \ CH_3\cdot \ + \ CH_2{=}\overset{+}{O}CH_2 CH_2 CN \ (m/e \ 84)$$

$$CH_3 CH_2 \overset{+\cdot}{O} CH_2 CH_2 CN \ \rightarrow \ CH_3 CH_2 O\cdot \ + \ \overset{+}{C}H_2 CH_2 CN \ (m/e \ 54)$$

$$CH_3 CH_2 \overset{+\cdot}{O} CH_2 CH_2 CN \ \xrightarrow{-\cdot CH_2 CN} \ \underset{\underset{CH_2 CH_2}{|\curvearrowright|}}{H \ \overset{+}{O}{=}CH_2} \ \rightarrow \ C_2 H_4 \ + \ H\overset{+}{O}{=}CH_2$$
$$(m/e \ 59) \qquad (m/e \ 31)$$

8.29. Masses 45, 73, and 87 probably have 2, 4 (?), and 5 carbon atoms each, and thus contain one oxygen atom each. The rings-plus-double-bonds value of each of these and of the m/e 129 ions should thus equal 1/2, so that they are saturated ions. $C_8H_{17}O^+$ cannot be the molecular ion; it is an even-electron ion. The m/e 112 ion is an odd-electron ion. Mass 130 might be M^+, but its abundance is within experimental error of that expected for the heavy isotope contribution of from m/e 129. The ion series m/e 31, 45, 59, 73, 87 suggests (Table A-4) that an alcohol or ether function is a dominant feature of the molecule; the lack of M^+ indicates (Table A-3) that this is not a straight-chain ether. A key clue is the "metastable ion" of m/e 96.7; for the transition m/e 130 → 112 a "metastable" would be expected at m/e 96.4 (m/e 129 → 112 would appear at m/e 97.0, but would involve the unlikely loss of 17 amu). This suggests that m/e 130 is the molecular ion, and that m/e 112 is the $(M - 18)^+$ formed by loss of H_2O from an alcohol. (The mass 130 could also be an odd-electron *fragment* ion, but this would predict a second functional group in the molecule, for which there appears to be no evidence in any of the peaks.) The abundant $(M - 43)^+$ and $(M - 57)^+$ ions indicate the identity of the octyl alcohol as C_4H_9—CHOH—C_3H_7; the lack of $(M - 15)^+$ and $(M - 29)^+$ ions indicate there is no chain branching. The other ions then present a consistent picture. [4-Octanol]

$$C_3H_7\overset{+\cdot}{\underset{\displaystyle \overset{OH}{|}}{CH}}{-}C_4H_9$$

→ $C_3H_7 CH{=}\overset{+}{O}H$ ⟶ $C_3H_7\overset{+}{C}H{-}OH$ → $H_2O + C_4H_7$
   m/e 73   *m/e* 55

→ $C_4H_9 CH{=}\overset{+}{O}H$ ⟶ $C_4H_9\overset{+}{C}{-}OH$ → $H_2O + C_5H_9$
   m/e 87   *m/e* 69

8.30. [Methyl *tert*-butyl ketone]
8.31. [Methyl methacrylate]
8.32. [Allyl acetate]

9.1. *A*: $R_1 = R_2 = R_3 = H$, $Y = H_2$;
        B: $R_1 = H$, $R_2 = CH_3O$, $R_3 = CH_3$, $Y = H_2$;
        C: $R_1 = CH_3O$, $R_2 = H$, $R_3 = CH_3$, $Y = O$; see Ref. *9.1.*

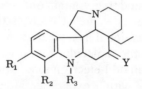

9.2. The *m/e* 45/47 ratio shows that the mass 45 ion contains no elements other than C, H, N, F, or P of Table A-2, and suggests that the isotopic contribution of *m/e* 44 to *m/e* 46 is negligible. The mass 46/45 ratio indicates 2 carbon atoms in *m/e* 45, for which the formula C_2H_7N is now the logical choice. This is an odd-electron ion, and none of the tests eliminates it as the molecular ion. Only two molecules are possible: $C_2H_5NH_2$ and $(CH_3)_2NH$. The base $(M - 1)^+$ makes the latter the obvious choice. [Dimethylamine, Ref. *1.17*, no. 1124]

$$H{-}CH_2{-}NHCH_3 \rightarrow H\cdot + CH_2{=}\overset{+}{N}HCH_3 \ \ m/e \ 44$$

9.3. Assuming roughly the same abundance ratios for masses 48/46 and 47/45, the isotopic abundance of masses 47/46 indicates the formula C_2H_6O for *m/e* 46. Here the $(M - 15)^+ > (M - 1)^+$, so the structure C_2H_5OH is more probable than CH_3OCH_3. [Ethanol, Ref. *1.17*, no. 424]

$$CH_3 \overset{\frown}{-} CH_2 \overset{\gamma \overset{+}{\cdot}}{-} OH \rightarrow CH_3 \cdot + CH_2 \overset{+}{=} OH$$

9.4. The m/e 150 ion appears to have C_7 and O_3 components; this is supported by apparent C_8 and O_3 components in m/e 165. The mass 104 peak has maxima of 7 carbon and 1 oxygen atoms. The m/e 43 ion isotope ratios point to the composition C_2H_3O. None of the tests eliminates m/e 165 as the molecular ion; it must then contain an odd number of nitrogen atoms. Masses 104 and 76 *may* be significant odd-electron ions. The molecule appears to be generally stable, giving a few abundant ions. Aromatic character is indicated by the low mass ion series. The abundant $(M - 15)^+$ indicates facile loss of CH_3, and the m/e 43 and $(M - 43)^+$ make the acetyl group, $-COCH_3$, a possible source of this loss. If the acetyl group is attached to the phenyl, this offers an explanation for the abundant m/e 104:

$$Y - C_6H_4 - CO - CH_3^{+} \rightarrow Y - C_6H_4 - CO^+ \rightarrow Y \cdot + C_6H_4CO^{+}$$

This decomposition of an even-electron ion to yield an abundant odd-electron ion is unusual, and requires Y to be strongly electron-attracting. Additional evidence comes from m/e 76; this is commonly formed from disubstituted aromatic compounds (*1.15*). If so, this second functional group contains $165 - (76 + 43) = 46$ amu, and is probably NO_2, $C_7H_4NO_3$ (m/e 150) $- C_7H_4O$ (m/e 104). Loss of NO is typical of nitroaromatics (Table A-5); m/e 120 may be $(M - CH_3 - NO)^+$, and m/e 92 may be $(M - CH_3CO - NO)^+$. [*p*-Nitroacetophenone]

9.5. Isotopic abundances give calculations of $C_{7.5}$, $C_{6.8}$, and C_4 for m/e 112, 97, and 57, respectively; the molecular formula is probably C_8H_{16}. Table A-4 and the low mass ion series are consistent with this. The ion $C_4H_9^+$ dominates the alkyl ion series; a *sec*- or *tert*-butyl group is possible. The $(M - CH_3)^+ > (M - C_3H_7)^+ >> (M - C_2H_5)^+$, so that the *sec*-butyl group is unlikely. A C_8H_{16} molecule containing a C_4H_9 group should also contain an olefinic, cyclobutyl, or methylcyclopropyl group. Even if this group activated the cleavage $C_4H_7-C_4H_9$ (e.g., an allylic cleavage), the large $C_4H_9^+/C_4H_7^+$ ratio indicates that the $C_4H_9^+$ is highly stabilized, that is, it is *tert*-butyl. However, it is dangerous to carry the interpretation too far without comparison with spectra of close isomers, because of the ubiquitous random rearrangements of hydrocarbons. (The m/e 56/55 ratio can be used as evidence for a 2-methylalkene. The reaction shown should be much less favored for the 1-methyl isomer.) [2,4,4-Trimethyl-1-pentene, Ref. *1.17*, no. 130]

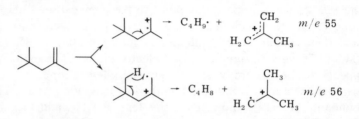

9.6 through 9.10. The molecular formula is $C_4H_8O_2$ in each case. Again it might be instructive to enumerate the possible compounds of this composition containing a carbonyl group, and classify them according to the expected C—O stretching frequency. The rings-plus-double-bonds value = 1, so that the molecules must be acyclic and saturated except for the carbonyl group. The possibilities include esters (1730–1750 cm⁻¹) $HCOOC_3H_7$, $HCOOCH(CH_3)_2$, $C_2H_5COOCH_3$, and CH_3-$COOC_2H_5$; alkoxy- or hydroxyaldehydes (1715–1740 cm⁻¹ *when not hydrogen-bonded*); $CH_3OCH_2COCH_3$ or hydroxy methyl ethyl ketones (1700–1720 cm⁻¹ *when not hydrogen-bonded*); and acids (1685–1710 cm⁻¹), C_3H_7COOH and $(CH_3)_2CHCOOH$.

Unknown 9.6 should be an ester; the $(M - 27)^+$ is the double hydrogen rearrangement peak typical of ethyl esters, and the other peaks (except m/e 70) are consistent with this structure.

For Unknown 9.9 the propyl formates are eliminated as they should yield m/e 47 ions by the same double hydrogen rearrangement. The "metastable" at m/e 37.1 corresponds to formation of the second largest ion by $88^+ \rightarrow 57^+ + 31$. Of the remaining possible aldehydes and ester, only $C_2H_5COOCH_3$, CH_3OCH_2-CH_2CHO, and $CH_3OCH(CH_3)CHO$ could give plausible reactions corresponding to these masses. The last should give a sizable $(M - CH_3)^+$ and a very abundant $CH_3\overset{+}{O}{=}CHCH_3$ ion; for $CH_3OCH_2CH_2CHO$ the $(M - 1)^+$ and m/e 45 should be more abundant. The high abundances of m/e 57 ($C_2H_5CO^+$) and m/e 29 ($C_2H_5^+$) strongly favor the ester.

The infrared spectrum suggests that the carbonyl group in Unknown 9.8 must be hydrogen-bonded; the base peak at m/e 29 and the $(M - 18)^+$ indicate the compound to be a hydroxyaldehyde. A β-OH is favored over α- or γ-OH by the abundance of m/e 45 as compared to m/e 31 or 59. This is borne out by the second largest peak in the spectrum, the odd-electron m/e 44 ion.

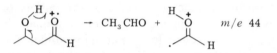

Unknown 9.10 has m/e 45 as its base peak; this most probably is CH_3CHOH— because of the low mass 31 abundance ($COOH^+$ would not be this abundant in comparison to $C_3H_7^+$ by comparative ion stabilities). The structure $CH_3CHOHCOCH_3$ is the only possibility remaining that contains this moiety, and the rest of the spectrum is consistent with this.

The remaining Unknown, 9.7, has its base peak at m/e 43. The remaining methyl ketone, $HOCH_2CH_2COCH_3$, is improbable because of the low abundance of m/e 58 and 31. The alternative assignment of m/e 43 as $C_3H_7^+$ is consistent with a butyric acid, the only possibility among the remaining structures. The large $(M - CH_3)^+$ and small m/e 60 (from a hydrogen abstraction rearrangement) support an iso structure. [9.6, Ethyl acetate, Ref. *1.17*, no. 387; 9.7, isobutyric acid, Ref. *1.17*, no. 650; 9.8, β-hydroxybutyraldehyde; 9.9, methyl propionate, Ref. *1.17*, no. 388; 9.10, 3-hydroxybutan-2-one]

9.11. The isotopic clusters indicate a chlorine atom in masses 166, 147, 116, 109, 97, 85, 66, and 47. Carbon contents are low: a maximum of C_3 in 166, 147, 131, and 93; C_1 in 69 and 31, and so on. Mass 166 is indicated as the molecular ion; the ion series fit those expected for chlorofluorocarbons, suggesting C_3ClF_5 as the molecular formula. Random rearrangements are common in such compounds, making assignments less secure unless reference spectra of similar compounds are available. Thus though the abundance relationship $(M - CClF_2)^+ > (M - CF_3)^+$ indicates a terminal $CClF_2$ group, the less indicative methyl ions show $CF_3^+ > CClF_2^+$ in abundance. Experience shows that the large $(M - Cl)^+/M^+$ ratio is indicative of allylic chlorine; in the

2-chloroperfluoropropene this abundance ratio is 0.5. [3-Chloroperfluoropropene, Ref. *1.17*, M.C.A. no. 130]

9.12. You may find that the solution of this spectrum is difficult. Check to see if you have assigned the formulas $C_3H_7O_2$ to m/e 75 and C_2H_5O to m/e 45. If not, rework the problem assuming these data were supplied by high-resolution mass spectrometry.

This spectrum is difficult because of the variety of isobaric formulas which can be applied to each major ion, and because of the absence of a molecular ion. Yet many students are able to arrive at the correct structure in a relatively short time, mainly because the data fit this structure so well. Without reference spectra it is difficult to eliminate many other possible structures unequivocally. However, such a "best guess" can often be very valuable.

The m/e 75 ion has no more than 3 carbon and 2 oxygen atoms; m/e 45 has no more than 2 carbon atoms. Despite its low abundance, the presence of any m/e 61 is strong evidence that m/e 75 is not the molecular ion. Additionally, molecular formulas such as C_3H_9NO and $C_2H_5NO_2$ necessary to fit an ion of m/e 75 are difficult to envision as giving the other ions found, such as m/e 31. Thus there appears to be no M^+. For such low molecular weight compounds the lack of M^+ suggests a saturated structure (Table A-4), so that CH_3O^+, $C_2H_5O^+$, and $C_3H_7O_2^+$ are the most favorable postulates for the abundant m/e 31, 45, and 75 ions, respectively. Thus m/e 75 must contain two functional groups; there is no odd-electron $(M-18)^+$ ion to indicate that either is a hydroxy group. The abundant CH_3^+ suggests a CH_3O moiety; relative ion stabilities predict a low abundance for CH_3^+ unless it is attached to an electron-attracting group. The CH_3O group is probably attached to —CH_2—, as it cannot be part of a $CH_3OCH(CH_3)$— or $CH_3OC(CH_3)_2$— group. If these groups were present the abundance of the m/e 59 or 73 ions, respectively, would be much greater than is observed. (To reiterate, never neglect the large amount of *negative* information present in every mass spectrum—it can be very valuable.) The few abundant ions in the spectrum suggest a simple molecular structure, so that there is a strong possibility that one of the two oxygen-containing functional groups in the m/e 75 ion is the same as the one in the m/e 45 ion. If there is no hydroxyl group, the most logical structure for the m/e 75 ion is $(CH_3O)_2CH—$ (see Ref. *1.15*), and for the molecule it is $CH_3OCH_2OCH_3$. It should be reemphasized that this was not a rigorous proof of structure by mass spectrometry, but rather a way to hypothesize a probable structure which can then be checked against reference spectra or other techniques. [Methylal, Ref. *1.17*, no. 1111]

9.13. The mass 122 ion appears to have 7 carbon atoms and 2 oxygen atoms, so it could be $C_7H_6O_2$, rings-plus-double-bonds value = 5. The m/e 104 ion possibly has 7 carbon atoms, and it should be noted as an odd-electron ion along with masses 94 and 76. Mass 122 seems to be a prime candidate for the molecular ion, and its abundance indicates a highly stable molecule. In the low mass region the predominant ion series indicates an aromatic hydrocarbon, so that the rings-plus-double-bonds value of 5 corresponds to a phenyl ring plus an additional ring or double bond. The striking $(M — 1)^+$ peak indicates the presence of a labile hydrogen atom, and $(M — 18)^+$ indicates a ready loss of H_2O (Table A-5 suggests this is due to a hydroxyl group). The $(M — 28)^+$ and $(M — 29)^+$ ions are probably $C_6H_6O^+$ and $C_6H_5O^+$, respectively, due to loss of CO, and COH, as losses of C_2H_4 and C_2H_5 would yield unusually unsaturated structures. The $(M — 29)^+$ suggests the —CHO group is present, which would account for the extra double bond predicted by the rings-plus-double-bonds calculation above. From these indications of a labile hydrogen, phenyl, —OH, and —CHO an obvious structure postulation is $HO—C_6H_4—CHO$, a structure which also is consistent with the m/e 76 ion, $C_6H_4^+$. The odd-electron ions m/e 104 and 94 indicate that this is the ortho isomer. [Salicylaldehyde]

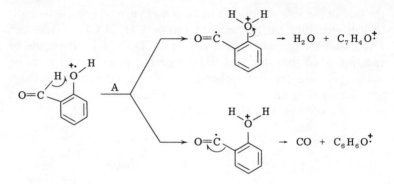

9.14. The m/e 188 and 160 ions each appear to contain one sulfur atom. Therefore m/e 188 is $C_{11}H_{24}S$ (saturated) or $C_{12}H_{12}S$ (rings-plus-double-bonds value = 7) and m/e 160 is $C_9H_{20}S$ or $C_{10}H_8S$. Odd-electron ions include the base peak at m/e 160 plus smaller peaks at masses 134, 128, and 110. Mass 188 fails no tests as the probable molecular ion. The great number of low m/e peaks seems confusing, but the large number and abundance of the doubly charged ions gives strong evidence for the highly unsaturated molecular formula $C_{12}H_{12}S$. In support of this there appears to be an aromatic ion series m/e 39, 50, 51, 52, 62, 63, 64, 76, although probably there are also substantial contributions to a number of these peaks from doubly charged ions. There is evidence for the extension of this series for other hydrocarbon ions that have a low H/C ratio, such as $C_7H_5^+$, $C_8H_6^+$, $C_9H_7^+$, $C_{10}H_8^+$, and $C_{11}H_9^+$, consistent with the fact that the molecule contains 3 more rings-plus-double-bonds than a single benzene ring. In checking for other low m/e ion series, note that the abundant m/e 45 is most logically CHS^+, and that many other ions can be similarly justified if the presence of sulfur is assumed, for example, $C_2H_2S^+$, $C_3H_3S^+$, $C_4H_4S^+$, $C_5H_3S^+$, $C_6H_6S^+$, $C_7H_5S^+$, $C_8H_6S^+$, $C_9H_7S^+$, and even $C_{10}H_8S^+$. This points to the sulfur as part of the highly unsaturated system of the molecule, such as in a fused ring aromatic. The base peak in the spectrum is due to the loss of C_2H_4. Table A-5 suggests either a hydrogen abstraction rearrangement for which one can at least draw some possible structures, as in (1) or a retro Diels–Alder reaction such as (2). If structures such as (1) are proposed,

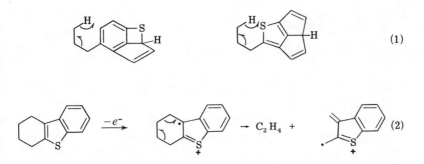

the $(M - C_3H_5)^+$ ion, m/e 147, must arise through some sort of a double hydrogen rearrangement. For the benzothiophene-type molecule of (2), elimination of $C_3H_5\cdot$ from the saturated fused ring with rearrangement could give the sulfur analog of the benzotropylium ion. It should be noted that it is entirely possible that quite different hydrocarbon structures than those postulated here could give prominent $(M - C_2H_4)^+$ and $(M - C_3H_5)^+$ ions because of the more random rearrangements that can occur with hydrocarbons. A relatively small amount of structural information from other sources could help considerably. [1,2,3,4-Tetrahydrodibenzothiophene, Ref. *1.17*, no. 1375]

9.15. The presence of at least two oxygen atoms and one nitrogen atom is required by the fact that this is the ethyl ester of an amino acid. The m/e 177/179 ratio suggests an isotopic cluster, and the abundances are consistent with 1 sulfur and around 8 carbon atoms for m/e 177. There is probably a sulfur atom in the peaks at m/e 148, 131, 104, and 61. To calculate the elemental composition, mass $177 - 32 (S_1) - 32 (O_2) - 14 (N) =$ 99, which would be C_8H_3 (impossible for an ethyl ester) or, more probably, C_7H_{15}. None of the tests eliminates m/e 177 as the molecular ion, $C_7H_{15}NO_2S$. Other odd-electron ions are difficult to identify because of the presence of the nitrogen atom.

The large number of functional groups present makes it more difficult to judge the significance of the low mass ion series. In the alkyl amine series m/e 30 appears to be the only ion of importance; this fact plus an appreciable $(M - 17)^+$ indicate a free amine group. Of the ion series of Table A-4 containing sulfur, the alkylthiol or sulfide series m/e 47, 61, 75 offer a structure

$$\overset{\underset{\displaystyle R-CH \overset{|}{\longleftarrow} COOC_2H_5}{}}{\overset{+\cdot}{NH_2}} \rightarrow R-CH=\overset{+}{N}H_2 + \cdot COOC_2H_5$$

assignment for the sulfur atom in the molecule. The $(M-15)^+$, $(M-29)^+$, and $(M-46)^{\ddagger}$ are roughly as expected for an ethyl ester. From Table A-5 the $(M-48)^{\ddagger}$ ion could be due to a methyl sulfide, and this supports the assignment of $CH_3SCH_2^+$ as the structure of the base peak at m/e 61 and for the group lost in m/e 116. The $(M-73)^+$ is expected for $R-COOC_2H_5$ when R^+ is stabilized, such as occurs for α-amino acids (Table A-5). The stable R^+ also accounts for the lack of the expected $(M-C_2H_4)^{\ddagger}$ and $(M-C_2H_3)^+$. $R-CHNH_2COOC_2H_5$ must have a mass of $177-102=75$, and must contain CH_3SCH_2-, so that the molecular structure $CH_3SCH_2CH_2CHNH_2COOC_2H_5$ is indicated. [Methionine ethyl ester, Ref. *1.3*, p. 274]

REFERENCES

1.1 J. H. Beynon, *Mass Spectrometry and Its Applications to Organic Chemistry* (Elsevier, Amsterdam, 1960).

1.2 J. H. Beynon and A. E. Williams, *Mass and Abundance Tables for Use in Mass Spectrometry* (Elsevier, Amsterdam, 1963).

1.3 Klaus Biemann, *Mass Spectrometry: Organic Chemical Applications* (McGraw-Hill, New York, 1962).

1.4 C. Brunnée and H. Voshage, *Massenspektrometrie* (Verlag Karl Thiemig, Munich, 1964).

1.5 H. Budzikiewicz, C. Djerassi, and D. H. Williams, *Interpretation of Mass Spectra of Organic Compounds* (Holden-Day, San Francisco, 1964).

1.6 H. Budzikiewicz, C. Djerassi, and D. H. Williams, *Structure Elucidation of Natural Products by Mass Spectrometry*: Vol. I, *Alkaloids*; Vol. II, *Steroids, Terpenoids, Sugars, and Miscellaneous Natural Products* (Holden-Day, San Francisco, 1964).

1.7 R. W. Kiser, *Introduction to Mass Spectrometry and Its Applications* (Prentice-Hall, Englewood Cliffs, N.J., 1965).
C. A. McDowell (ed.), *Mass Spectrometry* (McGraw-Hill, New York, 1963).

1.8 F. W. McLafferty (ed.), *Mass Spectrometry of Organic Ions* (Academic Press, New York, 1963).

1.9 Klaus Biemann, "Applications of Mass Spectrometry," *in* Arnold Weissberger (ed.), *Techniques of Organic Chemistry*, Vol. 11, pp. 259–316 (Wiley, New York, 1963).

1.10   Klaus Biemann, "Mass Spectrometry," *Ann. Rev. Biochem.* **32,** 755–80 (1963).

1.11   F. W. McLafferty, "Mass Spectrometry," in F. C. Nachod and W. D. Phillips (eds.), *Determination of Organic Structures by Physical Methods*, pp. 93–175 (Academic Press, New York, 1962).

1.12   F. W. McLafferty and R. S. Gohlke, "Expanded Analytical Horizons Through Mass Spectrometry," *Chem. Eng. News* **42,** 96–108 (May 18, 1964).

1.13   J. D. Morrison, "Mass Spectrometry and Chemical Problems," *Rev. Pure Appl. Chem.* **12,** 117–125 (1962).

1.14   Gerd Spiteller and Margot Spiteller-Friedmann, *Angew. Chem.* (Intl. Ed.) **4,** 383 (1965).

1.15   F. W. McLafferty, *Mass Spectral Correlations* (American Chemical Society, Washington, D.C., 1963).

1.16   R. S. Gohlke, *Uncertified Mass Spectral Data* (The Dow Chemical Company, Midland, Michigan, 1963).

1.17   American Petroleum Institute and the Manufacturing Chemists Association, *Catalog of Mass Spectral Data* (Chemical Thermodynamic Properties Center, Texas A. and M. University, College Station, Texas).

1.18   American Society for Testing Materials Committee E-14, *Index of Mass Spectral Data* (A.S.T.M., Philadelphia, 1963).
       Joshua Lederberg, *Computation of Molecular Formulas for Mass Spectrometry* (Holden-Day, San Francisco, 1964).
       D. D. Tunnicliff, P. A. Wadsworth, and D. O. Schissler, *Mass and Abundance Tables* (Shell Development Company, Emeryville, California, 1965).

2.1   F. W. McLafferty, *Science* **151,** 641 (1966).

2.2   Klaus Biemann, *Pure Appl. Chem.* **9.1,** 95 (1964).

2.3   R. A. Saunders and A. E. Williams, in Ref. *1.8*, p. 343.

2.4   Klaus Biemann, P. Bommer, and D. N. Desiderio, *Tetrahedron Letters* **1964,** 1725.

2.5   J. H. Beynon in J. W. Waldron (ed.), *Advances in Mass Spectrometry,* Vol. 1, p. 328 (Pergamon, London, 1959).

2.6   F. W. McLafferty, *Anal. Chem.* **28,** 306 (1956).

2.7   J. H. Brewster, Private Communication, Dept. of Chemistry, Purdue University.

2.8   J. H. E. Mattauch, W. Thiele, and A. H. Wapstra, *Nuclear Phys.,* **67,** 1 (1965).

3.1   Lewis Friedman and F. A. Long, *J. Am. Chem. Soc.* **75,** 2832 (1953).

3.2   J. S. Shannon, *Proc. Royal Austr. Chem. Inst.* **1964**, 328.

3.3   F. W. McLafferty, in Ref. *1.8*, p. 309.

3.4   V. Hanuš and L. Dolejš, Private Communication, Institute of Physical Chemistry, Czechoslovak Academy of Sciences, Prague, April, 1965.

3.5   C. E. Melton in Ref. *1.8*, p. 65.

3.6   F. W. McLafferty, *Anal. Chem.* **29**, 1782 (1957).

3.7   P. D. Zemany, *J. Appl. Phys.* **23**, 924 (1952).

3.8   H. D. Beckey *et al., Advances in Mass Spectrometry,* Vol. 3, p. 35 (Institute of Petroleum, London, 1966).

3.9   G. G. Wanless and G. A. Clock, *Anal. Chem.* **39**, 2 (1967).

4.1   H. M. Grubb and Seymour Meyerson in Ref. *1.8*, p. 453.

6.1   V. J. Caldecourt, The Dow Chemical Company, Midland, Michigan, has used such logarithmic recording for mass spectra since 1950.

6.2   R. T. Aplin, H. Budzikiewicz, H. S. Horn, and Joshua Lederberg, *Anal. Chem.* **37**, 776 (1965).

6.3   M. Barber and R. M. Elliott, *Proc. Mass Spectr. Conf. ASTM E-14* **12**, 150 (1964).

6.4   J. H. Beynon, R. A. Saunders, and A. E. Williams, *Nature* **204**, 67 (1964).

6.5   J. H. Futtrell, K. R. Ryan, and L. W. Sieck, *J. Chem. Phys.* **43**, 1832 (1965).

6.6   T. W. Shannon and F. W. McLafferty, unpublished results.

6.7   R. E. Ferguson, K. E. McCulloh, and H. M. Rosenstock, *J. Chem. Phys.* **42**, 100 (1964).

6.8   F. W. McLafferty, R. S. Gohlke, and R. C. Golesworthy, *Proc. Mass Spectr. Conf. ASTM E-14* **12**, 331 (1964).

6.9   J. H. Beynon, R. A. Saunders, and A. E. Williams, *Tables of Metastable Transitions* (Elsevier, Amsterdam, 1966).

7.1   N. B. Colthup, *J. Opt. Soc. Am.* **40**, 397 (1950).

8.1   F. W. McLafferty, *Anal. Chem.* **31**, 82 (1959).

8.2   F. W. McLafferty, *in* J. D. Waldron (ed.), *Advances in Mass Spectrometry,* Vol. 1, p. 355 (Pergamon, London, 1959).

8.3   F. W. McLafferty, *Anal. Chem.* **31**, 477 (1959); M. M. Bursey and F. W. McLafferty, *J. Am. Chem. Soc.* **88**, 529 (1966).

8.4   H. M. Rosenstock and M. Krauss in Ref. *1.8*, p. 1.

8.5   D. P. Stevenson, *Discussions Faraday Soc.* **10**, 35 (1951).

8.5a F. W. McLafferty, *Chem. Commun. (London)* **1966**, 78.
8.6   J. S. Shannon, *Austral. J. Chem.* **16**, 683 (1963).
8.7   R. S. Gohlke and F. W. McLafferty, *Anal. Chem.* **34**, 1281 (1962).
8.8   Klaus Biemann, Ref. *1.3*, p. 88.
8.9   H. Budzikiewicz, C. Djerassi, and D. H. Williams, Ref. *1.5*, p. 54.
8.10 F. W. McLafferty, *Anal. Chem.* **34**, 2 (1962).
8.10a G. A. Olah, C. A. Cupas, M. B. Comisarow, *J. Am. Chem. Soc.* **88**, 364 (1966).
8.11 F. W. McLafferty, *Anal. Chem.* **34**, 26 (1962).
8.12 C. Djerassi and Catherine Fenselau, *J. Am. Chem. Soc.* **87**, 5747 (1965).
8.13 H. Budzikiewicz, C. Djerassi, and D. H. Williams, Ref. *1.5*, p. 74.
8.14 Klaus Biemann, Ref. *1.3*, p. 102.
8.15 H. Budzikiewicz, J. I. Brauman, and Carl Djerassi, *Tetrahedron* **21**, 1855 (1965).
8.16 As designated in publications from a number of laboratories (*1.6*, *1.14*, *3.2*, *8.17*, *8.23*).
8.17 N. C. Rol, *Rec. Trav. Chim.* **84**, 413 (1965).
8.18 H. Budzikiewicz, Catherine Fenselau, and C. Djerassi, *Tetrahedron* **22**, 1391 (1966).
8.19 Seymour Meyerson and L. C. Leitch, *J. Am. Chem. Soc.* **88**, 56 (1965).
8.20 R. Ryhage and E. Stenhagen, in Ref. *1.8*, p. 399.
8.21 A. G. Harrison and E. G. Jones, *Can. J. Chem.* **43**, 960 (1965); C. Djerassi, G. von Mutzenbecher, J. Fajkos, D. H. Williams, and H. Budzikiewicz, *J. Am. Chem. Soc.* **87**, 817 (1965).
8.22 F. W. McLafferty, *in* R. N. Elliott (ed.), *Advances in Mass Spectrometry,* Vol. 3 (Pergamon, London, 1966).
8.23 Gerd Spiteller and Margot Spiteller-Friedmann, *Monatsh. Chem.* **95**, 257 (1964).
8.24 F. W. McLafferty, *Applied Spectroscopy* **11**, 148 (1957).
8.25 F. W. McLafferty and R. S. Gohlke, *Anal. Chem.* **31**, 2076 (1959).
8.26 E. M. Emery, *Anal. Chem.* **32**, 1495 (1960).
8.27 T. Aczel and H. E. Lumpkin, *Anal. Chem.* **34**, 33 (1962).
8.28 H. Budzikiewicz, C. Djerassi, and D. H. Williams, Ref. *1.5*, p. 194.
8.29 A. G. Sharkey, Jr., J. L. Shultz, and R. A. Friedel, *Anal. Chem.* **28**, 934 (1956).
8.30 F. W. McLafferty, *Anal. Chem.* **31**, 2072 (1959).

8.31   M. Fischer and C. Djerassi, *Chem. Ber.* **99**, 750 (1966), and references cited therein.

8.32   W. H. McFadden, K. L. Stevens, S. Meyerson, G. J. Karabatsos, and C. E. Orzech, Jr., *J. Phys. Chem.* **69**, 1742 (1965).

8.33   P. Brown, C. Djerassi, G. Schroll, H. J. Jakobsen, and Sven-Olov Lawesson, *J. Am. Chem. Soc.* **87**, 4559 (1965).

8.34   W. Benz and K. Biemann, *J. Am. Chem. Soc.* **86**, 2375 (1964); S. Meyerson and L. C. Leitch, *ibid.*, **86**, 2555 (1964), and references cited therein.

8.34b   W. H. McFadden and M. Lounsbury, *Can. J. Chem.* **40**, 1965 (1962); A. M. Duffield, S. D. Sample, and Carl Djerassi, *Chem. Commun.* **1966**, 193.

8.35   J. H. Beynon, G. R. Lester, and A. E. Williams, *J. Phys. Chem.* **63**, 1861 (1959); J. H. Beynon and A. E. Williams, *Appl. Spectroscopy* **14**, 156 (1960).

8.36   F. W. McLafferty and M. C. Hamming, *Chem. Ind.* **1958**, 1366.

8.37   S. M. Alam, K. A. H. Adams, and B. B. MacLean, *Can. J. Chem.* **42**, 2456 (1964).

8.38   C. Djerassi and Catherine Fenselau, *J. Am. Chem. Soc.* **87**, 5756 (1965).

8.39   H. Budzikiewicz, C. Djerassi, and D. H. Williams, Ref. *1.5*, p. 102.

8.40   T. W. Shannon and F. W. McLafferty, to be published.

8.41   C. Djerassi and Catherine Fenselau, *J. Am. Chem. Soc.* **87**, 5752 (1965).

8.42   A. M. Duffield, H. Budzikiewicz, D. H. Williams, and C. Djerassi, *J. Am. Chem. Soc.* **87**, 812 (1965).

9.1   K. Biemann, Ref. *1.3*, p. 309.

9.2   D. H. Williams, H. Budzikiewicz, and C. Djerassi, *J. Am. Chem. Soc.* **86**, 284 (1964).

9.3   M. St. C. Flett, *Characteristic Frequencies of Chemical Groups in the Infrared* (Elsevier, Amsterdam, 1963).

APPENDIX

TABLE A-1   *Standard Interpretation Procedure*

---

1. Study all available information (spectroscopic, chemical, sample history). Give explicit directions for obtaining spectrum.

2. Verify masses; determine elemental compositions, rings-plus-double-bonds.

3. Mark abundant odd-electron ions. Test molecular ion identity.

4. Study general appearance of spectrum; molecular stability, labile bonds.

5. Identify all low mass ion series.

6. Identify the neutral fragments accompanying high mass ion formation (including "metastables").

7. Postulate structures for abundant ions.

8. Postulate molecular structures; test against reference spectrum, against spectra of similar compounds, or against spectra predicted from mechanisms of ion decompositions.

TABLE A-2   *Elemental Composition*

Natural Abundances of Common Isotopes					
Isotope	Mass	%	Mass	%	Mass	%
H	1,	100	2,	0.016		
C	12,	100	13,	1.08		
N	14,	100	15,	0.36		
O	16,	100	17,	0.04	18,	0.20
F	19,	100				
Si	28,	100	29,	5.07	30,	3.31
P	31,	100				
S	32,	100	33,	0.78	34,	4.39
Cl	35,	100			37,	32.0
Br	79,	100			81,	97.5
I	127,	100				

Determination of Elemental Composition (*1.3*)

If only C, H, N, O, F, P, I present, and no interferences from other ions,

$$\frac{[(A + 1)^+]}{[A^+]} = \text{ca. } 1.1\% \times \text{no. of C atoms} + 0.36\% \times \text{no. of N atoms}$$

$$\frac{[(A + 2)^+]}{[A^+]} = \text{ca. } \frac{(1.1 \times \text{no. of C atoms})^2 \%}{200} + 0.20\% \times \text{no. of O atoms}$$

Examples:

$$C_5H_5N: \frac{[(A + 1)^+]}{[A^+]} = 5 \times 1.1\% + 1 \times 0.36\% = 5.9\%;$$

$$\frac{[(A + 2)^+]}{[A^+]} = \frac{5.5^2}{200}\% = 0.15\%$$

$$C_7H_5O: \frac{[(A + 1)^+]}{[A^+]} = 7.7\%; \frac{[(A + 2)^+]}{[A^+]} = \frac{7.7^2}{200}\% + 0.20\% = 0.50\%$$

TABLE A-2   (Continued)

Rings-plus-Double-Bonds

Elemental Formula: $C_x H_y N_z O_n$ (more general case
$I_y II_n III_z IV_x$, where I = H, F, Cl,
Br, I; II = 0, S; III = N, P; and
IV = C, Si, etc.)

Total rings-plus-double-bonds = $x - \frac{1}{2}y + \frac{1}{2}z + 1$

(For each element in its *lowest* valence state; see Section 2.6)
For an even-electron ion, the true value will be followed by "$\frac{1}{2}$"
(2.7)

Examples:

$C_5 H_5 N$: rings-plus-double-bonds = $5 - 2.5$

$+ 0.5 + 1 = 4$,
for example, pyridine$^{+\cdot}$ (odd-electron)

$C_7 H_5 O$: rings-plus-double-bonds = $7 - 2.5 + 1 = 5.5$,

for example, $C_6 H_5 CO^+$, benzoyl (even-electron)

TABLE A-3 Molecular Ion Abundances vs. Compound Type (C_n indicates a n-alkyl chain of n carbon atoms)

Compound Type	Intensity of Molecular Ion Relative to Most Intense Ion			M.W. for $[M^+] < 0.1\%$
	M.W. ~ 75	M.W. ~ 130	M.W. ~ 185	
Aromatic	[benzene] 100	[naphthalene] 100	[anthracene] 100	>500
Heterocyclic	[pyridine] 100	[quinoline] 100	[acridine] 100	>500
	[thiophene] 100	[benzothiophene] 100	[dibenzothiophene] 100	>500
Cycloalkane	[cyclohexane H] 70	[decalin H H] 88	[H H H] 90	>500
Mercaptan	C_3SH 100	C_7SH 39	$C_{10}SH$ 46	>>200
Sulfide	C_1SC_2 65	C_1SC_6 46	C_5SC_5 13	>>200
Conjugated Olefin	Hexatriene 54	Alloocimene 41	—	>500
Olefin	$C_2C{=}CC_2$ 36	$C_3C{=}CC_4$ 20 $C_6C{=}CC$ 7.3	$C_{11}C{=}C$ 3.3	>500
Amide	C_2CONH_2 56 $HCON(C_1)_2$ 100	C_6CONH_2 0.9 $C_1CON(C_2)_2$ 4.0	$C_{11}CONH_2$ 0.9 $C_1CON(C_4)_2$ 5.1	—
Acid	C_2COOH 78	C_6COOH 0.6	C_9COOH 9.4	—[b]
Ketone[a]	C_1COC_2 24	C_2COC_5 8.0 C_1COC_6 3.0	C_6COC_5 8.3 C_1COC_9 9.6	>500
Aldehyde[a]	C_2CHO 46	$C_x CHO$ 2.1	$C_{12}CHO$ 4.6	

212

	C_5	8.8	C_9	6.4	C_{13}	4.6	>500
Alkane	C_5	8.8	C_9	6.4	C_{13}	4.6	>500
Ether[a]	C_2OC_2	30	C_4OC_4	1.5	C_6OC_6	0.05	180
Amine[a]	C_4NH_2	10	C_8NH_2	0.6	$C_{12}NH_2$	2.3	[b]
	$(C_2)_2NH$	31	$(C_4)_2NH$	11	$(C_7)_2NH$	4.1	—
			$(C_2)_3N$	20	$(C_4)_3N$	6.7	—
Ester[a]	C_1COOC	19	C_1COOC_5	0.0	C_1COOC_8	0.0	[b]
			C_5COOC_1	0.3	C_7COOC_1	2.6	—
Halide	C_4F	0.07	C_7F	0.1			RF >120
	C_3Cl	4.3	C_7Cl	0.1	$C_{11}Cl$	0.3	RCl >300[a]
			C_3Br	45	C_7Br	2.4	RBr 300
			C_1I	100	C_4I	5.5	RI 320
Branched Alkane	C—C—C—C (with C branch)	6.3	$(C_2)_2CC_4$ (branched)	1.2	$(C_4)_3CH$	1.0	~400
	C—C—C (with two C branches)	0.01	(branched structure)	0.02	(branched structure)	0.03	70
Nitrile[a]	C_4CN	0.3	C_8CN	0.4	$C_{11}CN$	0.8	[b]
Alcohol[a]	C_4	1.1	C_8	0.0	C_{12}	0.0	90
Acetal[a]	$C(OC)_2$	0.00	$C_2(OC_3)_2$	0.0	$C_7(OC_2)_2$	0.0	All

[a] $(M + 1)^+$ possible (see Section 3.3).
[b] $[M^+]$ apparently increases with increasing molecular weight at higher molecular weight (see Section 4.1).

TABLE A-4   Series of Common Fragment Ions (Mainly Even-Electron)

m/e						Formula	Compound type
61	75	89	103	117	**131**	$C_nH_{2n+1}O_2$	RCOOR' (specific dbl. H rearr. loss of R'); ROR'OH, HOROH, ROR'OR'' (some specific[d])
47	61	75 75 76	89	103	**119**	$C_nH_{2n+1}S$	Alkyl thiols, sulfides (some specific[d])
63	77	91	105	119	133	$C_6H_5C_nH_{2n}$	Phenylalkyl (specific[d] cleavage, also rearr.)
			105	119	133	$C_nH_{2n+1}C_6H_4CO$	Benzoyl (specific[d]); 119 and above, unsatd. or cyclic phenoxy
63	77	91				$C_nH_{2n+1}O_3$	ROCOOR' (specific dbl. H rearr. loss of R or R', plus addnl. possible loss of R' or R by specific H rearr.)
78	92	106	120	134		$C_5H_4NC_nH_{2n}$	Pyridyl, aminoaromatic (specific cleavage, also rearr.)
50 50 51	64 65						See footnote c
			(79)				(m/e 79, $C_6H_7^+$, is a rearrangement ion for some substituted aromatics)
39 52							
39 53	67	81	95	109		C_nH_{2n-3}	Dienes, alkynes, cycloalkenes[e]

										Formula	
		40	54	68	81	95	109			$C_nH_{2n-1}O$	Furylalkyl (specific[d]); polyunsatd. or cyclic alcs. and ethers
					82	96	110	124	138	$C_nH_{2n}CN$	Nitriles
					83	97	111	125		$C_4H_3SC_nH_{2m}$	Thiophenes (specific[d])
	27	41	55	69	83	97	111			C_nH_{2n-1}	Alkenes, cycloalkanes[e]
				69							See footnote c
			55	69	83	97				$C_nH_{2n-1}CO$	Alkenyl-, cycloalkyl carbonyl (specific[d]); diunsatd., cyclic alcs., ethers[e]
			56	70	84	98				$C_nH_{2n}N$	Alkenyl-, cycloalkylamines[e]
15	29	43	57	71	85	99	113			C_nH_{2n+1}	Alkyl
	29	43	57	71	85	99				$C_nH_{2n+1}CO$	Satd. carbonyl (specific[d]), cyclic ethers[e]
	30	44	58	72	86	100	114	128		$C_nH_{2n+2}N$	Amines (specific[d]; also secondary rearr. rxs.)
						100					See footnote c
		44	58	72	86	100				$C_nH_{2n+2}NCO$	Amides, ureas, carbamates (specific[d], others)
	31	45	59	73	87	101				$C_nH_{2n+1}O$	Alcohols, ethers (some specific[d])
	31	45	59	73	87	101				$C_nH_{2n-1}S$	Thiacycloalkanes; unsatd., subst., S cpds.

[a] Cl and Br have been omitted as they are usually recognizable by their distinctive natural isotopic abundances.

[b] Specific cleavages giving a major peak are usually indicative of a particular structural moiety. Lower mass even-electron ions which are formed through secondary decompositions involving randomizing rearrangements are often of significant abundance, so that such ions are generally useful to indicate compound _types_, not specific structural moieties.

[c] Underlined values indicate masses typical of aromatic and many heterocyclic compounds. Boldface values indicate masses typical of perfluoroalkyls.

[d] Specific decomposition path as predicted by "new bond rule" (see Section 8.2).

[e] Might also be formed by H_2 or CH_4 loss from abundant series 2 mass units higher.

TABLE A-5 Common Neutral Fragments (Formed by loss from the molecular ion unless otherwise indicated)

m/e	Formula	Example
39 53 67	C_nH_{2n-3}	Allyl esters (dbl. H rearr.)
26 40	C_2H_2, C_3H_4	Aromatics
27 41 55 69, etc.	C_nH_{2n-1}	$RCOC_3H_7^+ \rightarrow RC(OH)_2^+ + C_3H_5 \cdot$ (rearr.); $(CH_3)_2 CHY$ (Y = OH, CH_2OH, CH_2COOR, etc.)
27	HCN	Nitrogen-heterocyclic compounds
28 42 56	C_nH_{2n}	$RCCH_2 C_3H_7^+ \rightarrow RC(OH)CH_2^+ + C_3H_6$ (rearr.); retro Diels–Alder
28	CO	Quinones, formates, $RC\!\equiv\!O^+$
42	CH_2CO	Unsaturated acetates, acetamides
43	HNCO	—NH—CO— from cyclic amides
1 15 29 43 57 71, etc.	C_nH_{2n+1}	Alkyl loss–cleavage at more highly branched site favored
29 43 57	$C_nH_{2n+1}CO$	$C_nH_{2n+1}CO\!\!+\!\!R$, where R^+ is stable
16	O	Sulfoxides, pyridine oxides; smaller for epoxides, nitro compounds, quinones
2 16 30 44 58 72, etc.	C_nH_{2n+2}	Loss of RH (R on branched site favored); loss of H_2 or CH_4 mainly from even-electron ion

Masses	Formula	Identity / Notes
30	NO	Nitroaromatics
44	CO_2	Anhydrides
44	$CONH_2$	$R\!\!\not\,CONH_2$ (stable R^+ only)
17	NH_3	Some amino acid esters; generally uncommon
17, 31, 45, 59	$C_nH_{2n+1}O$	$R\!\!\not\,OR'$ (stable R^+ only); $RCO\!\!\not\,OR'$
59, 73	CO_2R'	$R\!\!\not\,O\!\!\overset{\text{O}}{\underset{\|}{C}}R'$, $R\!\!\not\,COR'$ (stable R^+, small R' only)
18, 32, 46, 60	H_2O, $H_2O + C_2H_4$	Alcohols (primary favored), aldehydes; loss of ROH from some esters
60	CH_3COOH	Acetates
19, 33, 47	$C_nH_{2n}F$	Fluorides
47, 61	$C_nH_{2n+1}S$	$R\!\!\not\,SR'$, R^+ more stable than R'^+
20	HF	$R\!\equiv\!HF$
34, 48, 62, 76	H_2S, $H_2S + C_2H_4$	Thiols (primary favored); methyl sulfides
35, 49, 63	$C_nH_{2n}Cl$	Chlorides
36	HCl	$R\!\equiv\!HCl$ (distinctive Cl[37])
79	Br	$R\!\!\not\,Br$ (distinctive Br[81])
127	I	$R\!\!\not\,I$

217

TABLE A-6   *Metastable Ion Nomograph*

m/e 30–150 (3–15)

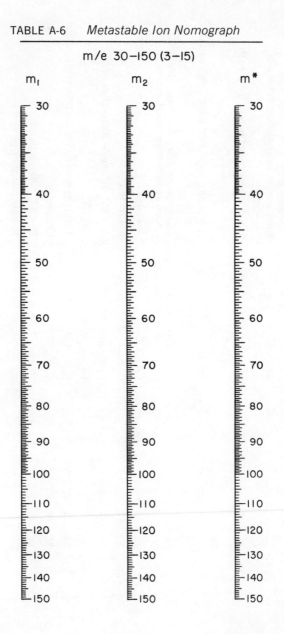

TABLE A-6 (Continued)

m/e 100–500 (10–50)

m_1	m_2	m^*
100	100	100
110	110	110
120	120	120
130	130	130
140	140	140
150	150	150
160	160	160
170	170	170
180	180	180
190	190	190
200	200	200
250	250	250
300	300	300
350	350	350
400	400	400
450	450	450
500	500	500

TABLE A-7   Common Odd-Electron Fragment Ions [a]

Mass number	Formula	Compound type
66 80 94	C_nH_{2n-4}	Cycloalkene≠YY', C_nH_{2n-4}≠YY'
68 82 96 110	C_nH_{2n-2}	Cycloalkyl≠HY, cycloalkyl≠YY', C_nH_{2n-2}≠YY'
41 55 126, etc.	C_nH_{2n-1} N	N≡CCHR+Z+H (nitriles)
	C_nH_{2n-14}	R-naphthyl≠HY*, R-naphthyl≠YY', R-naphthyl — C_nH_{2n-1}≠HY*
42 56 70 84 98 112 126	C_nH_{2n}	CHR=CR' CHR''+Z+H, cycloalkanes, C_nH_{2n}≠RY
98 112 126, etc.	C_nH_{2n-4} S	R-thiophenyl — CHR'+Z+H
44 58 72 86 100	C_nH_{2n}O	$\underset{\text{O}}{\text{R}\overset{\Vert}{\text{C}}\text{CHR}'}$+Z+H, O=C(CHR+Z+H)$_2$, CHR=CR'O+Z+H, C_nH_{2n}O≠HY
59 73 87 101 115	C_nH_{2n+1} NO	$\underset{\text{O}}{\text{RR'N}\overset{\Vert}{\text{C}}\text{CHR}''}$+Z+H, HON=CRCHR'+Z+H
46 60 74	C_nH_{2n}S	Cyclic sulfides, C_nH_{2n}S≠HY
60 74 83 102	C_nH_{2n}O$_2$	$\underset{\text{O}}{\text{RO}\overset{\Vert}{\text{C}}\text{CHR}'}$+Z+H, H+Z+OCCHR+Z'+H, C_nH_{2n}O$_2$≠RY

76	90 104 118 126, etc.	C_nH_{2n-8}
77	91 105 119 127, etc.	$C_nH_{2n-7}N$
	92 106 120	C_nH_{2n-6}
	92 106 120 134, etc.	$C_nH_{2n-8}O$

R-phenyl$\pm$HY*, R-phenyl$\pm$YY',
R-phenyl—$C_nH_{2n-1}$$\pm$HY*

R-pyridyl$\pm$HY*, R-phenyl—N(R')$\pm$YY', etc.
(see 76, 90, ...)

R-phenyl—CR'R''$\pm$Z$\pm$H

(—O—phenyl—R)$\pm$HY*, (—O—phenyl—R)$\pm$YY',

$$\text{R-phenyl—C(=O)CHR'}\pm\text{Z}\pm\text{H}$$

---

a Abbreviations: $\underline{R}$, H or alkyl group; $\underline{X}$, any halogen atom; $\underline{Y}$, a functional group; $\underline{Y}^*$, an electron-withdrawing functional group, e.g., $-\underline{X}$, $-\underline{NO_2}$, $-COOR$, $-CN$; $\underline{Z}$, a group from

which a H atom is rearranged, e.g., $RCCH_2$$\pm$Z$\pm$H could be $RCCH_2CH_2CH_3$; $\to$
$RC(OH)CH_2^+ + C_2H_4$. Common Z groups are $-CH_2CH_2-$, $-CH_2CH_2-$, $-CH_2O-$, $-OCH_2-$,

$-C(=O)CH_2-$, $-COR$, and analogs which are substituted or contain other heteroatoms.